John Milton

Books by Edmund Fuller

Fiction

A STAR POINTED NORTH
BROTHERS DIVIDED
THE CORRIDOR

Non-Fiction

GEORGE BERNARD SHAW: Critic of Western Morale
VERMONT: A History of the Green Mountain State
TINKERS AND GENIUS: The Story of the Yankee Inventors
MAN IN MODERN FICTION
BOOKS WITH MEN BEHIND THEM
A PAGEANT OF THE THEATRE
SUCCESSFUL CALAMITY
JOHN MILTON

Textbooks

ADVENTURES IN AMERICAN LITERATURE, Laureate Edition (with
    B. Jo Kinnick)
THE IDEA OF MAN (with O. B. Davis)
FOUR AMERICAN NOVELS (with Olga Achtenhagen)
FOUR NOVELS FOR ADVENTURE (with Olga Achtenhagen)
FOUR NOVELS FOR APPRECIATION (with Blanche Jennings
    Thompson)
FOUR ADVENTURES IN COURAGE (with Blanche Jennings
    Thompson)
FOUR AMERICAN BIOGRAPHIES (with O. B. Davis)
THREE WORLD CLASSICS (with O. B. Davis)
INVITATION TO SHAKESPEARE (a series)

JOHN MILTON

By Edmund Fuller

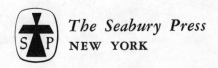

The Seabury Press
NEW YORK

TO MY WIFE
Ann Graham Fuller

Author's Note

THIS BOOK is a biography but in its attempt to bring John Milton before readers as a lively human being and to interpret his complex nature it employs some of the techniques of the novel. There is ample precedent for this from the father of biography, Plutarch, down to the present time. The earliest biographers presented orations and dialogues of their subjects where no text of such existed, basing these upon the best knowledge and traditions. Few modern biographies fail to take some of the interpretive liberties occasionally used here.

There is no transcript of what the young Milton said to Hugo Grotius or Galileo, or of what the older Milton said to Roger Williams or Oliver Cromwell. I have ventured to imagine these conversations, along with some more intimate family ones. But this has not been done lightly. In every case it has been based upon the established facts of Milton's life, or derived from opinions expressed in his own writings. No word has been placed in his mouth, no thought or feeling in his mind, for which there is not persuasive evidence to make it believable.

A great deal of study has gone into the effort to make this as accurate, as well as vivid, a life of Milton as available knowledge will permit. The same care has been given to the other characterizations in the book.

Contents

John Milton

Bread Street

TWO BOYS entered the courtyard of St. Paul's cathedral church and caused a flurrying flight among the countless pigeons that flocked there. The boys were cutting corners on their way to school. The blue-eyed, fair-skinned youth with light brown hair was John Milton, now in his fourteenth year. His companion was his opposite, darker of skin and white of teeth, eyes and hair a brilliant black. This was John's closest friend and schoolmate, Charles (Carlo) Diodati, son of the Italian physician who had come to London to attend the children of King James I. He was a few years older than the English boy.

St. Paul's housed the chief public school of the city, in this year 1622. It was principally for the sons of the well-to-do, but not beyond the means of John Milton, Senior, who sent both his sons there. He would educate them to the highest of callings, the clergy. So, almost two years before, at twelve, John had become one of "the pigeons of St. Paul's," the nickname the people of the city had given to the pupils bustling earnestly in and out of the cathedral.

The young Milton was a prodigy of learning who would have overshadowed most modern schoolboys by the broad, solid grounding of his knowledge. He was already set in the scholarly mold that was to shape his life. The harsh discipline of the rod, which was the order of the day in this school, was not needed to keep Milton at his tasks. He tells us himself that after the age of twelve he rarely stopped his studies before midnight. His chief tutor, Alexander Gill, became his lifelong friend.

For all this self-chosen ordeal of scholarship, a price would be paid throughout his life in the form of a shyness, sometimes well concealed but always present, in his dealings with people. It was the mark of a boy who had been overbrilliant, who had drawn too far from people and too close to books at too young an age.

The close companionship with Charles Diodati did much to save him. The older boy had in him the lightheartedness and gayety of his Italy, with none of the dark tones of temperament which Puritan influence had stamped upon Milton. The boys were always together, laughing at the differences in their lives and ways, but understanding one another, dreaming together over the plans of ambitious youth.

The life of London was their greatest book and they studied it together. They moved at the very hub of things, for a great part of London's affairs revolved around St. Paul's. It was not then like the later cathedral, of the famous dome, built by Sir Christopher Wren after fire destroyed the old one in 1666. It was built in the manner of the Gothic churches, in the shape of a cross. For a House of God it had fallen into use for strangely worldly traffic. It had three towers. Two were prisons. Beneath the third ran the area which was known as "Duke Humphrey's Walk," notorious for the evil lives and shady transactions of those who haunted it. Bawdy balladmongers hawked their wares along it and hucksters traded there. Had the Jesus who scourged the moneylenders from the Temple returned to this place He must again have taken up His whip of cords to purge His Father's House of these profaners. Pious souls declared the frequent bolts of lightning that fell upon the place to be signs of His wrath.

The Diodatis were Protestant Italians. The pressure of the

Inquisition had led the doctor to seize his chance to go to England. Charles told his friend fearful stories of religious terrorism. It was not hard for them to see the germ of evil in the cathedral where they went to their daily classes.

The whole dark, ugly city of London repelled the Italian boy as he roamed it with his friend. Italian cities had their slums and plague spots, too, but they had also their soaring beauties of architecture, their great monuments of culture. This London was still a walled city, in which a year-round guest was the plague, the dread Black Death. Outside the old Roman wall the ditch, or moat, was still to be seen, in some parts a stagnant pool, in other places filled in, as often as not, with rubbish and garbage. Within was a dark, wooden city of connected houses, sometimes ornate with gimcrack of the Middle Ages or Elizabeth's reign. People said the streets had been made for wheelbarrows and not for carts and coaches. In these narrow thoroughfares, the overhanging upper stories of the houses seemed to lean together and form an "umbrella of tiles" over the street. It was a joke that opposite neighbors could lean out their garret windows and shake hands. At the corners there were constant traffic disputes between rocking, high-slung stagecoaches and laden barrel carts.

Sewage ran down the middle of these streets and filth was dumped into them from upper windows. Rats flourished in the open gutters and the smell was not sweet. Yet John and Charles pried into every corner of the city, skipping the festering plague spots and fixing their eyes upon the eternal pageantry and excitement. Cheapside was the path of the many processions, religious or kingly, that wound their way through the city yearly. There was so much for the boys to watch: the vendors, hawkers and tinkers, the gingerbread makers, the scurrying apprentices busy mastering the many trades plied in the neighborhood, the puppet shows, and the religious plays.

This city of jumbled sights, smells, and sounds, sometimes festive, sometimes festering, always vibrantly alive, had been the total world of the boy Milton from his dawn of awareness. Bells were a permanent part of it, clamorous bells to rouse him from sleep and fetch him from the drift of dreams to the reality of bed, house, and streets. These bold, exciting bell songs were as much a part of his life as the ill-smelling London air. The rich tones from the tower of the church of St. Mary-le-Bow were the grandest, called "Bow bells" by all the city. By later tradition, the radius of the sound of Bow bells defined the origins and dwelling place of those people of London called Cockney. Mingled with them were deep tones from bells of the cathedral church of St. Paul, barely five minutes' walk away. Lesser voices from six other churches, all in the immediate neighborhood, blended in. Tired old folk sometimes cursed the racket but it was a boy's delight.

His father's house was on Bread Street. Neighboring streets in which the boy wandered had similar names: Fish Street, and Honey Lane Market with its booths of mouth-watering sweets. John had been very curious about the strange name of their neighborhood and one of its thoroughfares: Cheapside. Bread Street was an odd name, too.

His father had explained it all to him. "The ancient English word 'cheapen' means 'to buy,' my son. This is the part of town where the merchants gather, of all sorts."

"But why do we live on Bread Street?"

"Well, boy, the richest of the merchants keep their shops here. The finest inns are here for those who come from outside the city, or from anywhere in the world to buy and sell. It is a good place for a scrivener's shop, the best in the city."

"I mean, why is it called Bread Street? There is no bread here except what my mother bakes."

His father laughed and rumpled the child's hair. "No, there

is no bread here," he agreed. "It is only the strange way by which names come about. Longer ago than you could ever dream about—three hundred years—King Edward I forbade all the bakers of the city to sell bread in their houses or shops and ordered them to bring it to this street to market. So they called it 'Bread Street' and the name has stuck."

But if old Bread Street had lost the meaning of its name, the other streets of Cheapside had not. Poultry Street, Ironmonger Lane, Milk Street, Goldsmith's Row, Honey Lane Market, and Fish Street had been the stamping ground of the Milton children, John and Christopher and Anne, in their games and errands.

The Miltons were a respected family. John Milton, Senior, was no ordinary fellow. His father, Richard Milton of Oxfordshire, had been a Roman Catholic. The son had differed with him upon religious faith and, after his Oxford education, had gone to London. He hated the forms of Popery and even the high services of the Church of England. He began to lean toward the Puritans. It was into a Puritan household, therefore, that John Milton was born on the ninth of December, 1608.

Mr. Milton was a scrivener, that is, a public writer, who drew up contracts, leases, wills, and all such papers, and who sold legal stationery. There was a flourishing business of this sort to be done in Bread Street, as he had explained to his inquiring son. Under his scrivener's sign of the golden spread eagle John Milton prospered well enough to own this house and another in the country, to provide the best in education for his children, and to pursue his hobbies like a leisured gentleman.

Chief of his pleasures was music. He had real ability. Some of his compositions, sorrowful or sentimental songs, psalms, motets, or madrigals, have survived in collections of early English music and may yet be played and sung. Little John was brought up with a fine taste in music. Already the youngster could play upon the organ.

Daily a grave but kindly Puritan clergyman named Thomas Young came to tutor him. The boy learned swiftly and was soon educated quite beyond his years, reading Greek and Latin and trying his hand at literary composition. In later years, brother Christopher claimed that John had been writing poetry at ten.

This was the background from which young Milton had come to be one of "the pigeons of St. Paul's" with his Italian friend. In time Charles Diodati was finished at the school and went on to Oxford for medical studies, to follow his father's career. John said a sad good-by and turned inward still more to his studies and dreams. He wrote poems, now, paraphrases of the psalms of David, and he nursed bold visions of things he would do.

It was a rich life that he would lead, John Milton promised himself in daydreams over his books. He would go to Italy, for one thing, from a bright desire to see the sun-drenched land which had given him his friend. He would go to Italy, yes, perhaps with Charles himself to guide him through its treasures. And then he would return to England and would conquer it, conquer the very world so that it should never forget him. And his weapon would be his pen.

Chapter 2

The Rebel of Cambridge

C LOSE UPON his seventeenth birthday, a mounting excitement grew in John Milton. The school at St. Paul's was behind him, a landmark of mere boyhood. Now he stood upon the threshold of manhood and the prospect of college lay before him; happy prospect for this learned, earnest youth.

The thought was in his mind to go to Oxford, where his friend Charles had gone two years before. But his father was not content with this scheme. More and more rumors went around of the "Romish" ways of Oxford. Tighter and grimmer lines were drawing up throughout England between High and Low Church. To the Puritan-minded Miltons all that smacked of Catholicism or High Church of England was untrustworthy. The boy agreed. It was not for nothing that he had watched the wordly cheapening of the sacred walls of the cathedral. He had developed a scorn of bishops and religious pomp and circumstance.

Of the two great universities Cambridge was least tainted. So it came about that on February 12, 1625, the name of John Milton, son of John Milton of London, was written in the register of Christ's College, Cambridge.

On Bread Street, near his own front door, John took the coach, sitting high upon its top on the fine, clear day as any boy would do. As it rumbled down Cheapside and bumped over the rutted gutters of the lesser streets he took leave of the familiar surroundings, already bent upon visions of the new life before him. Out through the gates of the walled city and through the scattered suburbs the coach passed, into the green lanes and traveled highways of England, past the thatched cottages and rustic towns, northward.

It was a good day's journey. Cambridge lay some fifty-five miles north of London upon the very edge of the desolate fens or marshes that stretched beyond it into wasteland. The town was ancient, placed strategically at the fording of the river Cam, important to English travel since the Roman occupation. The university, with its many colleges, was already venerable.

The coach clattered into Cambridge with a scurry of dogs and children before it. Down from his perch climbed Milton, dusty and tired, but eager. The coachman grinned and called after him, "Good-by, lad. See that ye stick to your study bench as well as ye stuck to yer seat." The boy waved and laughed and hurried off. His luggage had been sent before him by cart. He had only to find his college.

He set off boldly down Trumpington Street. It would have been sensible to stop at the inn and make sure of his way, but this was not his mood this evening. His course took him down by the placid river. Along both sides of its bank were clustered several buildings, built long before Elizabeth's time and beautiful. Two of them were joined by an arched and covered span across the water. He stopped to gaze.

A group of students were strolling toward him. Milton hailed them, "Is this Christ's College?"

They laughed among themselves with the self-satisfaction of those who know their way around. One of the students pointed to the covered bridge. "Don't you know the Bridge of Sighs?" he demanded. "This is St. John's College, and the best at Cambridge."

"As for that," thought John, "there is room for opinion." Then, aloud, he asked, "Which is the way to Christ's?"

They pointed down a street which led away from the river

bank. Lost in the evening spell of Cambridge he passed among buildings of the other colleges. His spirit walked with Marlowe, the youth whose "mighty line" had rivaled Shakespeare's for perfection, who even in Cambridge had begun the career of plots and intrigues that was to strike him down with his song scarcely begun.

Christ's College was on Bridge Street, facing the ancient square tower of St. Andrew's Church. John stopped in the long shadow of the massive, arched gateway with its graven coat of arms. These were the portals to those halls that held the strong food for which his mind hungered. So it seemed to him.

He passed under the arch and found the garden chamber of the master of the college, Dr. Thomas Bainbrigge. The good doctor was pompous. "Well, sir?" he demanded, when John was admitted.

"I am John Milton, sir, from London."

"John Milton, eh? John Milton, London." The master groped on his desk for his record of registry. "Here we have you," and scanning the note he began to ask again for the information already before him. "What is your father?" he demanded.

"A scrivener, sir." Milton flushed and added, on impulse, "And musician."

"Scrivener, eh? Musician? I see nothing here about music."

"Scrivener by profession, sir," Milton repeated, "but a musician also, by love."

"Musician by love, eh?" Dr. Bainbrigge laughed. "Very well. Now the question will be, is his son a scholar by love? Yes, that will be our question. Now then, you will study with Mr. Chappell. He will give you a room. Mr. Chappell!"

The Reverend William Chappell had entered the chamber. He came forward at the master's summons and gazed at Milton with austere unfriendliness.

"This is John Milton, Mr. Chappell. He is your pupil, and I hope a likely one. Will you be good enough to find room for him?"

Without words, the tutor led John from the doctor's study. The students were quartered according to their length of time in the college and in keeping with this he found himself led to a cramped room in an attic. There were four beds here. Upon each of them sat one of his roommates to be, studying the new arrival with frank curiosity. With a bare nod to the others and a brief word of advice the Reverend William Chappell left John Milton here and departed. He was installed at Cambridge!

Clang, clang! Clang, clang! The morning bell began to drive the shadows of sleep from John's mind. It often seemed to him, in the hazy moments of unwilling awakening, that he was hearing again the rich, blended tones of the Bow bells, with the harmony of lesser chimes, that had rung through his days of boyhood.

It was dark as death at five o'clock in the morning, although March had drawn to its close. Groans and lamentations came from his mates in the attic room. Milton lit the lamp as the college bell ceased its brief ringing. By this faltering, timid light the four boys saw the grizzled steward who leered at them from the doorway. "Well, masters, well, gentlemen, up and out with you! Be at it! No slouching at the college. Your fathers were better men. I roused 'em all!"

A badly aimed shoe clattered harmlessly against the door-sill, followed by a heartfelt curse. The gleeful, cracking voice, happy with malice at arousing sleep-bound youth, could be heard at the next door along. "Come, lads, up and out with you! No slouching now!"

The young men scrambled into their clothes and hurried out to crowd with their fellows down the narrow stairs to the lecture halls. Two hours there would be of it, now, religious lectures and exercises until seven. Then, freed by their tutors, back to their rooms for breakfast, quick and plain.

From breakfast till noon in the classrooms, each group with its tutor; lectures and exercises. Then trooping together again, into the dining hall, to line up on uncomfortable, backless benches at the long trestle tables. And after dinner—freedom. Two hundred young men flocked out of the college halls to pass the afternoon in their chosen ways.

The college was crowded now. Besides the First Court, in which Milton was quartered, there was an ancient, wooden structure, significantly called Rats' Hall. Where this stood, later years would see a Second Court. But the student body still overflowed and, though oldsters scowled at the impropriety, a fortunate number were gaily housed in an inn called the Brazen George, opposite St. Andrew's Church.

There was a wide choice for the young bloods of Cambridge. Some went straight to the bear pits. This was a prime sport of the time, the matching of bears against one another, to wrestle and fight or to be baited by dogs, or men with whips or lances. Some chose boxing. The quiet waters of the Cam offered rowing, swimming, or fishing. Some clung to the Brazen George for roisterous drinking, or for smoking, which was still a novelty, though Virginia tobacco was beginning to take its hold on Englishmen.

Driving or riding was the choice of some, the clients of one of Cambridge town's rare figures, Thomas Hobson. This was the university carrier, who did a brisk business hiring out horses, boots, bridles, whips, and whatever else the slim-pursed rider might need. The students of Cambridge were hard riders and Hobson was a shrewd manager. He kept forty horses. When a customer came, the worthy carrier led him to this stable of great choice. Without regard to pleas or bribery he re-

quired each man to take whichever horse was next to the stable
door. His animals were used in rotation and no one horse was
ridden to death. A fine impartiality was observed toward all
customers. This practice was long to outlive Hobson. It has
come down to us in the expression "Hobson's choice" for anything of the "take it or leave it" sort.

John chose fencing as his chief exercise and sport. He spent
an hour or so daily with the skillful master of foils. He had the
feel of the blade and quickly gained an expertness that gave his
master keen respect for the lithe, quick, fair-skinned youth.

Yet there was only so much time for this. Milton had come
to Cambridge with a burning desire for learning. He was shy,
withdrawn somewhat within himself, and did not know how
to make friends easily. Other students were cool toward him at
first. He was hurt by this and his fighting spirit turned the pain
into scorn and fierce pride. He rarely joined the other boys in
sports. The afternoons of liberty found him chiefly in the shadowed library. In his mind there was a growing sense of purpose
—a flowering power of ego—which would have been unpleas-
ing had there not been in him the scope and stature and ability to justify it. But private intimations of immortality are not
the stuff from which hearty, popular personalities are made.

In the evening the little community was gathered together
for services. At nine o'clock in winter, ten o'clock in summer,
all were in bed. This was the order of the day at Christ's
College. The leisurely hours of the afternoon took the sting
from study and made of the college a pleasant fellowship for
most of its young men.

The curriculum fell into three divisions. There was the *Triv-
ium,* which covered grammar, rhetoric and logic; and the
Quadrivium, arithmetic, geometry, astronomy, and music,
which seems oddly tagged on in such an assortment. Added
to this were the broad subjects of theology and philosophy. It

seems forbidding enough, but it did not please Milton. The approach to the studies was lifeless and uninspiring. He thought the methods, the exercises, and the end results stupid. The philosophy and theology lectures were arbitrary and useless arguings over theoretical differences. It was an elaborate training in hairsplitting and the technique of counting angels on the heads of pins.

John was disappointed, and as the months of his study lengthened his disappointment grew more keen. His was a nature made for sterner stuff. He reckoned up the totals of his studies and found them lacking. So he was bound to make his voice heard. He began, with the brashness of his learned seventeen years, to criticize the courses. A student "beef" is common in colleges, but such "beefing" as Milton did was formidable. Instead of the expected classroom exercises, prim and perfect, he wrote attacks against the college. He drew up programs calling for living studies, "noble speaking and brave action." He called for the smashing of the narrow, academic walls that imprisoned minds and dry-rotted them. The world and its life, the heavens, the stars must be used in education: "Follow the wandering sun as his companion and call time itself to a reckoning and demand an account of its eternal march."

This was strong meat that Milton wished to serve up to his startled tutor. The Reverend William Chappell was no man to stomach such a dish. He determined to gag John Milton.

With the blessing of Dr. Bainbrigge, he summoned the rebel to his quarters. The slender boy stood before him with firm-set face. Mr. Chappell tried to scowl him down.

"Master Milton," he said grimly, "you are an undisciplined, umbrageous, heretical, and disorderly person in this college. You have caused the danger of confusion and unrest by your talking and writing."

"I have only said what I think, sir."

"You have only thought what is false and outrageous. You have challenged superior minds, older minds, and minds in authority. The word for this persistent course, sir, is impudence! I say gross impudence!" A deep flush had spread over the tutor's face. "This is not a university in which gross impudence may go unpunished. Turn your back!"

Milton clamped his lips shut to check his angry impulse toward defiant words. Let them do the thing their way. He obeyed the order silently. Seizing a rod with swift fury, the Reverend Chappell laid on a furious barrage of blows across the boy's back. No sound escaped John. Nothing was heard in the chamber but the thrashing blows and the heavy panting of the tutor.

At last he ceased and gasped for breath, the choleric tinge high in his cheeks. "Now, sir," he said hoarsely, "I think we shall have an end of your rash and dangerous thoughts."

"Not while I still think them," said Milton, so quietly that the tutor barely heard the words.

So it was that not long afterwards, in the spring of 1626, little more than a year after his entrance, an unrepentant, still rebelling John Milton found himself bound for London and his father's house. He was suspended from the University of Cambridge.

"At last, dear friend, your letter comes to my hand . . ." begins a long Latin letter from Milton to Charles Diodati, during his absence from the college. His lively friend had written warmly urging him to make the most of his holiday and have a good time to show for it. This was advice that Milton was in a fine mood to follow.

"Not now am I concerned to revisit the reedy Cam, nor am I harrowed now by love of my Lares [his cherished possessions] there, this long time denied me. I find no pleasure in fields that are naked and refuse soft shade. . . . I am not minded to bear unceasingly the threats of an unbending teacher and all the other trials that are not to be met by a nature such as mine. If it be exile for a man to visit his home, his father's house, and free of all anxieties to pursue the delights of leisure, then I refuse not the name of exile, nor, if you will, the *lot* of exile; nay, right merrily I enjoy the terms imposed by 'exile.' "

So, Master Milton is looking up! The sometime somber young Puritan scholar has kicked over the wagon and pursues even his soberest aims in his own free style. ". . . For I am privileged now to give, here, hours free of all else to the calm Muses, and my books—my true life—sweep me off with them, mastering me utterly. Presently, when I am weary grown, the splendour of the rounded theatre welcomes me, and summons me to sound its plaudits. . . ."

Here is a thing indeed! With Shakespeare scarcely ten years dead, with the last hearties of the Elizabethans still in their prime: Jonson and Dekker, Massinger, Ford and Fletcher, the rounded theaters might well capture John's heart. Their works were alive on the boards in daily rotation.

The "wooden O's," the doughnut-shaped open theaters, had not yet given way to the covered style. There were many of them in London, mostly on the south bank of the Thames where they had been out of reach of the civil authorities. There was the New Globe. (The famous old one had been destroyed by fire from a cannon, shot off during a performance of *Henry VIII* some years before. It was this occasion about which Sir Henry Wotton, later Milton's friend, reported that "one man had his breeches set on fire, that would have perhaps broyled him, if he had not by the benefit of a provident wit put it out with a bottle of ale.") There were also the Fortune, the Swan, the Red Bull, and the Bear Garden. The latter had its stage on trestles so that it could switch from plays to bearbaiting.

John gloried in these, this spring of 1626. New, popular hits were on the boards, plays that survive today, *A New Way to Pay Old Debts,* and *Rule a Wife and Have a Wife.* Any sunny afternoon was likely to find Milton dickering with the avaricious watermen who rowed spectators to the theaters and bear pits across the Thames.

More than all this, the blossom-scented spring forced the youth to another confession to the trusted Charles. Not only theaters and libraries found him haunting them. "A grove too claims me, a grove thick grown with elms, near the city, and the glorious shade of some spot not remote from the town. There o'er and o'er one may see troops of maidens pass, stars, these, that breathe forth alluring fires. Ah, how oft have I gazed spellbound on some marvellous form. . . ." John Milton was feeling his oats.

His one long letter to Charles tells the whole story of his forced holiday. The spirit of the times, the youths of the seventeenth century and the manner of their education, are all reflected in this exchange of letters. Two boys poured out to each other the secret confidences of their hearts and minds. Yet these thoughts of youth, these long, long thoughts, passed between them encased in grim Latin and ballasted with a heavy cargo of classical reference and lush prose. Truly this was an age!

But the richly spent holiday is closing. John must listen again to the stern call of his secret vision of destiny. "I am resolved," he admits with a note of regret, "to make my way back to the reedy marshes of the Cam and again to face the uproar of the noisy School."

Stern-fibered though he was, the Reverend William Chappell was of no mind to welcome back his granite-willed student and wear out his arm with canings. So it was by cordial consent that John, returning, was transferred to the care of another tutor, Richard Tovey. No private warfare broke out between these two and such further quarrels as Milton had with the college were wholly against the system. He never altogether ceased attacking the Cambridge approach to education as long as he was there. His hatred of it carried over far into his after life.

Bitter and satiric writings, which curled the hair of his teachers, continued to drip from his pen in the routine assignments of study. The students were given, as exercises, the writing of obituaries and elegies upon the deaths of bishops and other High Church figures. Milton performed these tasks with gusto, expressing his contempt for the high clergy in a heavily sarcastic lushness of style and overladen grief.

November fifth was observed for many years in England as Guy Fawkes' Day, the anniversary of that date in 1605 when Guido Fawkes, better known as Guy, had figured in the Catholic plot to blow up the houses of Parliament, King included, on the opening session. Fawkes, who was caught red-handed in the secretly gunpowder-filled cellars of Parliament, has been hanged and burned in effigy on this day ever since.

Undergraduates in the universities always wrote lampoons and comic pieces for the occasion. True to form, John wrote a fierce-voiced Latin poem against the spread of Romish sentiments in the college. It was an experience for the worthy tutors of Christ's College to have beneath them this grim and terrifying youth who impudently threatened them with the thunders of a Puritan God.

There had to be another side to this medal. Long after coming to the college, Milton had led a lonely life. In a ballot for student popularity he would have shown at the end of the list. He was not much liked, especially just before and just after his suspension.

The young man was slender and strong, skilled in his chosen activity of fencing, but not vigorous by nature. Sober-mindedness still warred within him against the easy goodfellowship of those around him. The spark of youth was strong in him, but partly hidden under a misfortune of his temperament. He did not know how to have a good time. The shyness and secret lack of confidence with people, hangovers from his study-wearied childhood, were handicaps to him. On the other hand, the proud, fierce side of him rushed into the gap to protect this lack from hostile eyes. It made him arrogant, a bit haughty, and sometimes a little pompous. He built his structure of security on the powers of his brilliant and noble mind. He drew around himself an invisible ring to keep off intruders.

John was shy. This was partly true with his fellow students, but oh, most particularly, with young women! By his own confession this learned young Puritan had a sharp eye for beauty. But his bold spirit quailed in the presence of girls and secretly shamed him.

Love struck him hard in his later Cambridge days. It insolently stalked him on the high street and ambushed him in the chambers of his heart. The names of his idols, if he was bold enough to learn them, he guarded in close secrecy. But once more, the Italian Diodati, the medical student from the nation of bold lovers, was the secret confidant.

To Charles he wrote: "Diodati—and I tell thee in amazement at myself—that same scornful I, who have always shown contempt for Love and have been wont to ridicule his wiles, have fallen into that trap which ensnareth on occasion the best of men."

On the fragrant mornings of May, he laments, "Lo, Love stood at my bed, tireless Love, with spangled wings." The merciless god tormented him by leading across his path multitudes of town or country girls, all beautiful, each more so than any other. Over and over his undisciplined heart leapt out. But always, "the lass who alone of lasses pleased now my tortured soul was withdrawn from my gaze, ne'er again to return to mine eyes."

The romantic Puritan had persuaded himself of a safeguard. He had accepted the alluring idea of unrequited, silent love. For if one's soul found its greatest outlet in the bleeding heart of love unfulfilled, it followed that one need not expose one's weakness by taking any steps to fulfill love. So John suffered pleasingly and safely.

All this was matter for his secret heart or for far-off, trust-worthy Charles. For the rest of the world, and for his worldly fellows, this would never do. This was a chink in the armor, a break in the invisible wall, that must not be discovered.

So it came about that one of the most personable young men of Cambridge, John Milton, with the fair, sensitive face and luminous eyes, he who might have led a string of fainting feminine hearts, gave out the notion that he scorned the women so dear to the hearts of the others. Sneeringly chaste and above-all-that was he, while the lesser sort might trot around with their idle courtships and affairs of the heart.

Now chastity and virtue are delicate blossoms. Milton vaunted them like coarse, great-stemmed sunflowers. It was offensive. The other youths of the college, lustily partaking of its sports and pastimes, or frequenting the friendly beer casks at the Brazen George, were quick to strike out at Milton's attitude. They named him "the Lady of Christ's."

This was a misunderstanding. The label was undeserved by Milton and did not stick long. His popularity grew steadily after his first couple of years at the college. It was his fair claim that when he came to the end of his seven year stint, he left behind at Cambridge real regret at his departure. It was not that Milton changed. Rather, his fellows "got on to him" and made up their minds that he might be a bit out of the way, but he was all right. They came to trust and respect him and proved their feeling by electing him to leading parts in college activities.

On one of the first of these times he brought the old feud into the open to dispose of it. He had been elected Master of the Routs, the festivities and ceremonies marking the end of the summer term. This was proof of his accepted position. His duty was to deliver a long, humorous Latin oration. The humor of the matter is doubtful. This was most of all the quality which Milton lacked. All his attempts at comedy were woefully heavy-handed in the rough and coarse style prevailing then, from classical examples. It was a concession, as he frankly said.

". . . If by chance I should swerve from my habit, if from the rigid laws of modesty, as they say, a finger's breadth, be it known, fellow students, that I have stripped off and laid aside for a short time my former custom out of good feeling for you."

In this same address he undertook to explain himself. "From some I have lately heard the epithet 'Lady.' But why do I seem to those fellows insufficiently masculine? . . . Doubtless it was because I was never able to gulp down huge bumpers in pancratic fashion; or because my hand has not become calloused by holding the plough-handle; or because I never lay down on my back under the sun at midday, like a seven-year ox-driver; perhaps, in fine, because I never proved myself a man in the same manner as those gluttons. But would that they could as easily lay aside their asshood as I whatever belongs to womanhood."

Pleasanter days followed as he drew closer to the other students. One of the best of his friends at the college was Edward King, son of a knight high in the service of Charles. There was both rivalry and friendship between them. King, being a gifted scholar and less of a rebel and challenger than John, sometimes won over him in the race for academic honors. It made no difference to them and they journeyed out together often into the fen country along the banks of the Cam.

John busied himself, now, with poems outside the exercises and assignments of the school. He had written two affectionately humorous pieces about Old Hobson, who had died, some said, from sheer fretfulness when an outbreak of the plague in London interrupted, for a time, his busy tasks of public carrying back and forth between college and city. Poems in English, Latin, and Italian, about everything from religion, to love, to philosophy began to gather on Milton's desk.

John was maturing. He was learning the technique of rough fighting in argument, that was to serve him well in stormy times for England. More than anything else he was the poet, convinced of a poetic destiny for himself. Half his battles were on the faith that art was of more importance than the meaningless studies of the college.

The reality of English life and politics was beginning to show itself to him. Something tense was in the air, cropping out in different ways at different times in different places, but shaping into a pattern to those who had the vision to understand it. Milton was not yet one of these but he had eyes.

Shortly after John had first come to the university, King James had died. Even at the ceremonies of mourning, the boys of the college were wondering about the new king, Charles I, and bandying the rumors that his wife was a secret Catholic, that the King himself leaned toward Rome.

Charles' reign was stormy from its beginning. He was not a Roman Catholic, but his vision of the Church of England and its proper forms of worship seemed almost indistinguishable from "Popery" to extreme Puritans, whose numbers were growing. Even without the open presence of the Roman Church in England, religious civil war was in the making.

King James had held that kings rule by divine right. Charles was even more insistent upon this view and pressed further to what he believed followed logically from it, the claim that the king can do no wrong. Thus he was impatient of parliaments and resistant to their pretensions to authority. He would tolerate Parliament as a debating society, as a body that would support the king, that might make requests, or even flatter itself that it counselled the king. But that it should claim genuine power, or set itself in opposition to the king was inacceptable to him as a matter of principle.

England was nearly at a halfway mark between an almost absolute monarchy, which was Charles' conception of his role, and constitutional monarchy in which the Parliament governs while the monarch simply "reigns" as a type of figurehead or symbol of the state, which is the case in England in our time. These differing conceptions of government, with Parliament increasingly jealous of its independent powers, added to the religious dissensions which also found King and Parliament on different sides, were a clash of powers and beliefs that had little chance of being resolved peacefully.

On the political side, Charles' chief adviser and strong-arm man was Sir Thomas Wentworth, first Earl of Strafford. At first he had been a Parliament man, one of the foremost opponents of the New King's policies. Soon he changed camps, receiving rapid promotions to positions of power, both political and military. Within a few years he had earned the ugly nickname of "Black Tom Tyrant."

In religious matters the King's chief support was William Laud, a churchman of impatient nature and brilliant abilities. Already a bishop when Charles came to the throne, he was advanced rapidly through more and more important sees (a "see" is the area of a bishop's jurisdiction) to that of London, and then of Canterbury where, as Archbishop, he was the head of the Church of England except only for the King himself.

Archbishop Laud wished to reform many aspects of worship and order in the Church of England that had fallen into neglect or abuse. By temperament haughty and high-tempered, he used his authority harshly. The law dealt severely with any who failed to conform to the worship of the Church of England —as did the Puritans of various groups. Fines, imprisonment, and even mutilation were the punishments meted out to nonconformists. Private religious services in the home were not safe from prying agents of the Archbishop. From one end of the kingdom to the other there was a cautious outward show of religious obedience, coupled with increasing dissent. The movement of groups of Separatists from England to Holland, and then on to New England, had begun under James and increased under King Charles and Archbishop Laud.

State and church affairs became entangled. One incident came close to John Milton. An intimate associate of the King, the Duke of Buckingham, who was hated by many of the opposing party, was assassinated in 1628. Milton's friend and former tutor at St. Paul's, Alexander Gill, was seized by order of Archbishop Laud and imprisoned for writing a poem against Buckingham. Gill was expelled from the priesthood, stripped of his degrees, fined heavily, and sentenced to lose his ears— one of the common forms of punishment. The pleas of his old and respected father finally caused him to be spared in the matter of the fine and the ears. Others were not so lucky. Milton was angered by what happened to his friend. Though the murdered Duke had been chancellor of the university, Milton refused to write the customary obituary, or elegy, which was expected of the students.

In 1629 Milton accepted his Bachelor's degree, with many required oaths of allegiance to King and Church of England, but he was not made, nor did he seek to become, a Fellow of the university. In their eyes he was a rebellious troublemaker. For his part, he rejected the expected thing at Christ's College, the taking of holy orders. He felt himself superior in abilities and integrity to many of his fellow students, who were flocking into the fold of Archbishop Laud. That was not the course for him.

At the age of twenty-three he finally left the university, adorned with his Master's degree. His last public statement at Cambridge, his valedictory, still sounded the creed of his own, personal ministry: "To be the oracle of many nations; to have one's house a kind of temple; to be such as kings and commonwealths invite to come to them, such as neighbors and foreigners flock to visit, such as to have even once seen shall be boasted of by others as something meritorious."

Chapter 3

"Growing My Wings and Meditating Flight"

Now it is the summertime—flourishing time for the young poet. It is more of a song singer than scholar who travels home from Cambridge. He will study still, but in his own good time and way, as he had done before in the brief days of his suspension.

It is not to hot, confining London that he goes but to his father's country home at Horton. This is July, 1632. The country is ripe with the English summer. The elder John Milton and his wife have settled there to live out their days quietly. Seldom, now, does the old man go into the city. He has retired prosperously. The scrivener's shop on Bread Street is managed almost entirely by a partner.

John was in a mood for ease and pleasure before plunging into the hard tasks he planned to set himself. It would do no harm, for a short while, "to loaf and invite his soul" as a later poet would say. To soak up for awhile the spirit and lore of the countryside would freshen the springs of his song.

Horton was in Buckinghamshire, on the river Colne, some seventeen miles from London. In easy walking distance was Windsor, with its castle, the ancient seat of English kings. Not far away was Eton, famous preparatory school whose playing fields, in Wellington's boast of later years, would produce the victorious warriors of Waterloo.

At Windsor, his admired Shakespeare had pitched the scene

of paunchy Falstaff's wooings. There the Merry Wives had plotted the downfall of the fat, lecherous knight.

Also near by was the marshy meadow of Runnymede. Beside it was the island in the Thames on which King John, whose subjects had muttered that his presence would befoul Hell, was humbled by his barons and forced to sign the Magna Carta, that Great Charter which is a cornerstone in the structure of English liberty.

The closeness of these ancient landmarks and the rich stuff of English folklore fed Milton's mind and made it ready to create majestic fantasies. They rooted to the soil of homeland the broad-spreading fabric of classic legend in which he was already schooled. He knew the farm folks' tales of elves and kobolds and the little men. He knew the raids of Queen Mab and her fairy folk upon the milk curds and treasures of the dairy house. The mischievous, pinching sprites were known to him and the treacherous lights that led men off their proper paths at night. He was acquainted with the wise investment of a nightly bowl of cream set out, for which the good goblin would labor until cockcrow threshing the corn or doing the household chores.

Dawn would often find him on some hillside watching the flaming sunrise and chatting with the plowman or shepherd beginning their long labors before the midday heat became too cruel. He heard the echoing hunter's horn and saw the long train of hounds and horses as the chase went by. Mower and milkmaid saw him wandering as they worked. He came in the evenings or on the days of festival and watched their country dances, drinking ale and telling tales with them with no Puritan's austere reproof upon his face.

The elder Milton was worried. When was this son of his, scholar though he was and brilliant too, going to set his feet upon the path of some proper career? He had been after all, seven years at Cambridge. Now it seemed as though, after a brief idleness, he was bent upon becoming a one-man, private university and studying forever. Not that he lacked the means for his son to live in leisure, but was it altogether fitting and respectable?

He rose from breakfast one morning and looked out the window. John had risen before him and was now stretched upon the grass with the volume of Greek history he had lately carried with him everywhere. Perhaps if he put forth a feeler he would learn something of his son's intentions. He went out.

John looked up at his approach. "Good morning, Father."

"Good morning, John." The father hesitated. There was such purpose in his son's features that it seemed hard to question him. Still, he would like to know. "Will you give me leave to interrupt your studies?"

"Certainly, sir." The young man put aside his book and sat up on the grass. "Sit down beside me, Father, if you wish to talk. The ground is quite dry."

"I hope it will not put a damp into my bones, but I will risk it." He stopped and cast about in his mind for a beginning. His son waited courteously. "Well, my boy, you should know that I am proud of you." He stopped again. This time Milton helped him.

"You have always been generous with approval, Father. I don't need a sudden assurance now. I think you must mean that you have some worry or concern and that you hesitate to name it. If you will tell me I will answer you the best way that I can."

"Very well, boy. I think it's time we should consider what plan you have, what profession you intend to enter. It's clear you will not be a clergyman, and with the spread of popish ways in the English church you have my support in so refusing. But then what are we to make of you?"

If I confess to him my whole purpose now, Milton was thinking, it will be of little help and will only disturb and trouble him the more. Aloud he answered, "For the present, Father, study is my purpose. Whatever course I may take, I feel the need of it. If you have no reason to be displeased with me I ask your permission for it."

"Study, my boy, I treat with reverence and could not rebuke you for. But you have studied already more than most men. Perhaps too much love of learning may be a fault. It would be a barren course to dream away your years in studious retirement, though I might afford to support you in it."

"You would be right, Father, if there were nothing else in it but mere curiosity of knowing. There are so many easier courses, so many frivolous ways of spending time, that surely a determined path of scholarship must have some clear and worthy end to it. I wish that you could trust me in it."

"I trust you, John. It worries me only for your own sake and for the sake of the world's opinion of you. It concerns me for your own success and happiness."

"I am very mindful of all those myself. I want the world's good opinion and mean to have it. Custom may call upon me to look for some work. I have, as much as any man, the natural wish for a house and family of my own. But I cannot take a quick or easy way for this. Let me show you something."

He rose and hastened into the house. Rummaging among the scattered papers on his desk he found a sheet of paper and went out with it.

"This, Father," he said, handing it to him, "may show you that I have not been without suspicion of myself, and that I have noticed a certain lateness in myself. It is a simple stanza done while I was at Cambridge. Let it partly speak for me."

His father took the paper and began to read the sonnet written upon it.

How soon hath Time, the subtle thief of youth
Stol'n on his wing my three-and-twentieth year!
My hasting days fly on with full career,
But my late spring no bud or blossom shew'th.
Perhaps my semblance might deceive the truth
That I to manhood am arrived so near. . . .

Yes, the elder Milton thought to himself as he read, the thing
is good; well considered and well built. As he read on in this
poet's pledge of accomplishment, "be it less or more, or soon or
slow," he felt he must yield to the intense sureness of his son's
will.

"Well," he said slowly, "your sonnet is good, John. You must
follow your own mysterious guideposts. I will not interfere."

The buds and blossoms of his "late spring" were now appear-
ing only a short time after the plaintive note of the sonnet. One
had a belated flowering. Two years before, at school, he had
written a sonnet in praise of Shakespeare. Now the young poet
was truly honored, for in the important Second Folio Edition of
Shakespeare, published in 1632, this sonnet was printed
with two other tributes by other poets. No stone memorial
was needed for the great poet, said his young successor:

Thou in our wonder and astonishment
Hast built thyself a livelong monument.
. . . .
And so sepulchred in such pomp dost lie,
That kings, for such a tomb, would wish to die.

It was scarcely an original thought. The confident Shakespeare
had said it for himself in one of his own sonnets:

Not marble, nor the gilded monuments
Of princes, shall outlive this powerful rime. . . .

but still, it was fitting that a poet destined to rank close after him should find early publication in praise of his peer.

During that summer in Horton he wrote two of his most-read and best-loved works, the paired poems of contrast, *L'Allegro* and *Il Penseroso*. It is easy to see how they grew out of this summer's ease, observations, and reflections. They are an astonishing leap to poetic maturity, no longer promise but fulfilment, the full blossom of the "late spring" his sonnet had lamented. They were his longed-for sign "That I to manhood am arrived so near." From the 325 lines of the two together come some of the most-quoted phrases of English poetry.

The poems place side by side two distinct types of man. The titles are Italian. *L'Allegro,* "The Cheerful Man," celebrates gaiety in its most appealing pleasures. He invokes Euphrosyne, "Joy," or as he prefers here, "Mirth," one of the Graces of Greek mythology.

> Haste thee, Nymph, and bring with thee
> Jest, and youthful Jollity,
> Quips and cranks and wanton wiles,
> Nods and becks and wreathèd smiles,
> Such as hang on Hebe's cheek,
> And love to live in dimple sleek;
> Sport that wrinkled Care derides,
> And Laughter holding both his sides.
> Come, and trip it, as you go,
> On the light fantastic toe;
> And in thy right hand lead with thee
> The mountain-nymph, sweet Liberty;
> And, if I give thee honour due,
> Mirth, admit me of thy crew,
> To live with her, and live with thee,
> In unreprovèd pleasures free. . . .

He sings, too, of "hounds and horn cheerly" rousing "the slumbering morn." Happy, too, are the ploughman's whistle, the milk-maid's song, the beauties of shepherd and shepherdess, the dancing in shaded bowers until nightfall, the "spicy nut-brown ale."

Stories are told by the shepherds:

> How Faery Mab the junkets eat.
> She was pinched and pulled, she said;
> And he, by friar's lantern led,
> Tells how the drudging goblin sweat
> To earn his cream-bowl duly set,
> When in one night, ere glimpse of morn,
> His shadowy flail hath threshed the corn
> That ten day-labourers could not end. . . .

He invokes wedding feasts with

> pomp, and feast, and revelry,
> With mask and antique pageantry;
> Such sights as youthful poets dream. . . .

as who knew better? Also he praises the pleasures of the stage:

> If Jonson's learnèd sock be on,
> Or sweetest Shakespeare, Fancy's child,
> Warble his native wood-notes wild.

And when the catalogue is complete, he ends with the promise:

> These delights if thou canst give,
> Mirth, with thee I mean to live.

Il Penseroso, "The Meditative Man," wants no such frivolities. He elevates Melancholy, here personifying sober thoughtfulness, to the rank of goddess and invokes her:

> Hail, divinest Melancholy!
> Whose saintly visage is too bright
> To hit the sense of human sight,
> And therefore to our weaker view
> O'erlaid with black, staid Wisdom's hue.

Milton mingles personages and images from classical myths and biblical and Christian tradition. His Melancholy springs from the Olympian gods but she is also compared to the black-robed nun. The "fiery-wheelèd throne" of the prophet Ezekiel's biblical vision is guided by "The Cherub Contemplation," whose name, bestowed by Milton, must be sounded "Con-tem-plày-she-own," so that the line will scan.

The pleasures of this thoughtful man are found in quiet, homely scenes

> Far from all resort of mirth,
> Save the cricket on the hearth.

His joy is in books, seeking "The spirit of Plato." The theatre of this man is solely the tragic stage where

> Sometime let gorgeous Tragedy
> In sceptred pall come sweeping by,
> Presenting Thebes, or Pelops' line,
> Or the tale of Troy divine. . . .

and whatever else

> . . . great bards beside
> In sage and solemn tunes have sung.

Milton pays tribute also to a great poet of an earlier age, Chaucer, with whom he would be linked along with Shakespeare, as the foremost trio of English poets.

If not in the scholar's quiet house and hearth, then this goddess Melancholy is to be sought in studious cloisters with

> storied windows richly dight,
> Casting a dim religious light.
> There let the pealing organ blow,
> To the full-voiced quire below,
> In service high and anthems clear.

His final goal is to

> Find out the peaceful hermitage,
> The hairy gown and mossy cell

and his promise is:

> These pleasures, Melancholy, give;
> And I with thee will choose to live.

Each man sings the praise of his chosen way. Each is committed absolutely and in his opening words denounces the other way with harsh hostility: "Hence, loathèd Melancholy," and "Hence, vain deluding Joys."

It's clear that both of these men dwell within the poet. They are the two halves of the divided and struggling Milton who never learned how to establish peace and compromise between them. At this time of writing, L'Allegro's part in him is, and for one or two years to come will be, at its greatest strength, but is destined to lose ground. Though both are in him they are more accurately two parts than two halves, with the equality that implies. L'Allegro lived on in Milton's mind, in poetic statement, but his truer temperament was Il Penseroso, who would triumph.

Like all men of letters of the time, Milton now kept a Commonplace Book, or journal of notes, speculations, and sketchy projects for literary works. This was not a diary, but a workbook; a storehouse and reminder. It was filling up with surprising matters for a young man seemingly so absorbed in the Muses.

It showed that he did not think highly of King Charles, or of the growing closeness between the church and the state. He made notes upon the republic as a form of government. There are speculations as to whether there might be divine approval of murder under some circumstances. There was a vague project for a tragedy drawn from the ancient history of Britain. All these things were witness that Christ's College had had only puny studies to offer besides those he chose for himself. This was a mind forever breaking out of bounds.

John went up to London for one of his frequent trips, to search for books, buy music, attend the theater, and do a host of other errands. In the shop of Curlett the music seller he made his purchases and was starting out the door. Wrapped in thought, he did not see the man who started to enter at the same moment. They came up short within an inch of one another's noses. Before John knew what he was about, the other had flung up his hand and shouted, "Milton!"

Looking up, startled, Milton returned the hail in kind, "Lawes!"

The two young men drew aside out of the shop door with a great slapping of backs.

"Now what brings you here?" demanded Henry Lawes.

"You could guess my errands well enough to trail me from shop to shop," declared Milton. "I might as well ask what brings you to Curlett's."

"Well, and why not? Could you guess whether I come to buy or sell? In faith, I'm here merely to inquire if the scoundrel has sold some wretched handful of my songs."

"Ha, then! I defy him to deny it and refuse you payment, for I have three of them myself, Harry."

"Charity, John, charity. I know you buy them only to keep a poor musician alive."

"If he were a poor musician, Harry, I'd let him starve."

"Grim, terrible critic," cried Lawes in mock horror. "I half believe you, Puritan. But you are the man I want to see. Your coming saves me the horrid tedium of letter writing, which would be useless anyway for I know you read nothing but Latin, which barbarous tongue I refuse to use for correspondence. Come over to the tavern."

They were well met, for this was one of Milton's favorite London acquaintances. Henry Lawes, some eight years older than the poet, had already become widely popular as a composer. His reputation was deserved for he is remembered as one of England's foremost musicians of the seventeenth century. The place they entered was one of those taverns of London celebrated as the haunts of great conversationalists. Some of the richest table talk in England was heard in these dingy, friendly taverns. There was no better place for old friends to go to balance up their accounts of mutual information.

"Whom do you see these days in London?" Lawes demanded as soon as they were seated.

"Barely anyone; Gill, sometimes; a few others. It is a rare chance to find you."

"Ah, well, I must admit, if I had not stumbled on you here you would have found me in a day or so more on your doorstep in Horton. I would have sought you out."

"For what fell purpose, Harry, or what happy circumstance?"

"To ply your trade of poet, John, and lend a hand to me."

"How so?"

"I am commissioned for the music for a masque within the month, at Harefield House, not ten miles from you on the Colne."

Milton nodded, "Yes, the dowager countess of Derby."

"The grand old dame must not be slighted on her birthday. It's not the same as Bess's time, or even James's, but she must have her due. You must write a masque for my tunes."

Milton was startled. "Don't joke with me, Harry. I have never written a masque!"

"Well write one now! There's no trick to it, for you. I want your brand of verses, my friend, as I've seen them in the few scant samples you have sent to me from time to time. Moreover, it will please the Countess to be celebrated by a neighboring poet. It will carry the good old soul back forty years."

"They say she was a rare, great beauty," Milton said, with half a sigh.

"You have seen her?"

John nodded.

"And you think it possible?"

"Yes, she has the grace of beautiful age."

"Excellent. If you believe it, all the better for your masque. We are agreed then?"

"All right," said Milton, "I will do it."

Working closely with Harry Lawes, Milton completed, in a short time, the brief masque *Arcades*. Barely more than a hundred lines, it is a hymn to the beauty and grace of the aging Countess. The young poet went proudly to the festivity to hear his lines spoken by young kinsfolk of the Countess. The setting was superb for its simple, unexcited beauty. The spacious grounds of Harefield, with their subtle flavoring of bygone days, quite won him. Here Elizabeth had once come to witness just such a pastoral. The ancient avenue of elms down which some of his speakers strolled was still known as the Queen's Walk. The event was altogether a success. In Milton it wakened an appetite for more.

The masque was a very special sort of theatrical entertainment. Plotless, unconcerned with vigorous action, it was chiefly the vehicle or mere excuse for a lavish pageant. It was highly formal, and deliberate in pace, accompanied by music and punctuated by songs. For the most part it was allegorical and dealt with virtues, and sentiments, and mythical persons.

If it seems strange that such an anemic form of drama should be hot upon the heels of the violent, roaring Elizabethan plays, it is because it was wholly a courtly proposition. It reached its peak under the Stuart kings and was the glorification of display for the sake of display. Costumes, settings, and ingenious stage effects drew more attention than the words and music in most cases. A great masquing hall was built in London, and in the formal gardens of castles and estates they were the pastimes of summer evenings.

For bread and butter, most of the playwrights then at work turned out a masque or two. Best of the lot, at this, was that same Ben Jonson whose rich-textured comedies are immortal on the English stage. Milton, who admired Jonson after Shakespeare, must surely have seen some of rare Ben's masques.

The great man in this field was the versatile Inigo Jones, architect and scene designer extraordinary. The rich and detailed backgrounds, the strange effects, of his creation were not to be equaled anywhere but in the lavish court theaters of Italy from which the whole fashion of the masque had sprung.

All this Milton well knew. But the masque had never been touched by a spirit such as his. He felt an inward challenge to take the thing and make of it something it had never been before and would never be again. *Arcades* was not it; it was a mere taster. He waited for the opportunity.

This was not long in coming and it came, quite naturally, from the same source. Lawes was an honest man, not unwilling to share his glory with an equal talent. He had been pleased with the first collaboration. About a year later, in 1634, he found himself again in need of a poet, for a more ambitious project. He was commissioned to compose music for, and to stage, a masque at Ludlow Castle, Shropshire, close to the border of Wales.

He came hastily to Horton, in the late summer, and put his need before Milton, who needed no urging. The poet had long been looking for the occasion and was ready. He delivered to Lawes, in due time, the piece which had no title except the one under which it was later published: "A Masque presented at Ludlow Castle, 1634, on Michaelmas Night, before John Earl of Bridgewater, Lord President of Wales." It has since been known to the world as *Comus*.

Milton journeyed off to Ludlow to watch the growth of this newest child of his expanding dreams. In the high-arched stone hall of the time-mellowed castle the patient Harry conducted such rehearsals as he might manage. It was the great handicap of masques that their actors were, for the most part, gentry or the very nobility themselves. Royalty, even, sometimes deigned to perform. Such persons could not be kicked about with the cavalier brusqueness of journeyman stage folk who plied the actor's trade.

In this case it was the three youngest children of the Earl himself who carried the burden of the play; the young Lord Brackly, his brother, Thomas Egerton, and their sister Alice. The other chief role Harry had shrewdly taken to himself, to keep some hand of practiced authority firm upon the proceedings. The courtiers and attendants of the castle were the "extras" who filled out the body of the larger scenes.

So motley, skylarking a crowd were not well disciplined to the stately dignity of *Comus*. But Lawes was casehardened. He entreated and cajoled, and by his tactful skill drew the performance into a shape that was not displeasing even to the critical eye of its excited author. For wild horses could not have dragged from the proud, shy poet a confession of the meaning of this event to him. Only keen, experienced Harry Lawes perceived it and loved his friend for it. The artist knew his brother in art. He was aware of the high spirit burning in these lines so lightly memorized for an evening's festival by the well-bred, casual youths.

September twenty-ninth was the climactic moment. The huge hall was richly decked out. In the place of honor sat the Lord President of Wales, with all members of his family not taking part in the entertainment. The sweet, stringed melodies of Harry's music crept over the hall. John Milton's fable was unfolded.

It was a tale of melancholy beauty. Harry Lawes, in the role of the "Attendant Spirit," related the slight story. The youngest children of a great king, the Lady and her two noble brothers, were making their way to the palace of their father. The journey led through the threatening, dark forest which was the masque's chief setting. This shadowed haunt was the dwelling place of dire Comus, child of the wine god, Bacchus, and Circe, the dread sorceress of the Mediterranean, upon whose isle Ulysses narrowly escaped the mishap of being turned into a swine. It was the habit of Comus to tempt all wayfarers with enchanted drinks, which inflicted them with the heads and natures of various beasts, while leaving their bodies in the human form. This hideous pack of victims, beastly and sinister in their transformation, were his unholy court.

Into the hands of Comus falls the Lady. She will not taste the treacherous cup. So rare is her purity that the enchanter's spells are powerless. He can do no more than freeze her spellbound in a chair. Coming to the aid of the helpless, distressed brothers, the Attendant Spirit invokes Sabrina, a virtuous nymph, who appears and banishes Comus and his evil throng, releasing the Lady from her imprisonment. Safely, then, the Attendant Spirit conducts them to the revels in progress at their kingly father's court.

This is the simple substance of the masque. But its pale and delicate story is encased in limpid verse and noble meditations which made all discerning persons know that a major poet had arisen to claim his place in England. This was the first great triumph of John Milton. Its impact was not yet felt in full.

The courtly assemblages were not of a mind to listen weightily to the virtuous counsel this young poet had to offer. They liked the masque, indeed, but liked it casually, hearing the words as little more than a pleasing part of the gentle tunes with which Lawes garnished them.

To these idle ears John had sung of virtue and the "unpolluted temple of the mind."

> Virtue could see to do what virtue would
> By her own radiant light, though sun and moon
> Were in the flat sea sunk.

Boldly the young Puritan chided the cavaliers and bade them walk in the path of his example.

> Mortals, that would follow me,
> Love Virtue; she alone is free:
> She can teach ye how to climb
> Higher than the sphery chime;
> Or, if Virtue feeble were,
> Heaven itself would stoop to her.

Author-like, John sat obscurely and bit at his nails as the unpracticed voices and ill-learned roles did violence to the perfection of his lines. Young Thomas Egerton cut him cruelly by "going up" in his part and dropping entirely the treasured speech, so near to Milton's heart, beginning, "How charming is divine philosophy, Not harsh and crabbèd as dull fools suppose." The Lady Alice stammered out the calm lines supposed to prove the unshaken, virtuous faith of the fair virgin. But this was little to any but the fond poet. To Harry Lawes it was familiar. With skill and wit, as the Attendant Spirit, he coached and prompted with so practiced a hand that none who watched knew of each minor crisis. The masque was a success. What did it matter, for the night, that none present knew that a new genius had bestowed upon the artificial form its greatest specimen and chief reason for remembrance?

Word soon spread about this lovely poem. Harry Lawes found himself besieged by requests for copies of it. He copied it, or had it copied, again and again in the next few years. Finally, in 1637, in sheer despair, he had it published by his own arrangements. For a second time Milton was in print, and once again, for the time being, anonymously, although there was no real secret of its authorship. It brought him wide esteem from many quarters.

One of these proved valuable. Provost of nearby Eton was old Sir Henry Wotton, one of the rarest worthies of his day. The old gentleman had heard of *Comus* and begged a copy of it. He was quick to see what manner of hand was here at work and lost no time in sending for Milton and befriending him.

Sir Henry was a man well qualified to judge of verse and help a budding poet. Poor, but distinguished, he was a minor poet and a major diplomat. He had helped to save King James from a poison plot when that monarch was merely ruler of Scotland. Wotton had hurried all the way from Florence with a warning and Italian antidotes for poisons. The grateful James, upon ascending England's throne, offered him the Embassy of Madrid or Paris.

Wotton was no fool. These were rich men's posts, calling for lavish outlays from a private purse. He chose the post in Venice, in the Italy he knew so well. Now, in retirement, he led a quiet life of scholarship. He was a lover of the rod and reel, and Milton, when walking, had more than once seen him in company with that Compleat Angler, gentle Isaak Walton, fishing in a bend of the Thames known as "Black Potts."

The old gentleman was one of the wits of his day. He had caused a minor scandal by his famous definition of an ambassador as "an honest man sent to lie abroad for the commonwealth." "Hanging," he had quipped another time, "was the worst use a man could be put to."

With John he spent many hours of pleasing conversation, unfolding stories that more than ever whetted the boy's appetite for that Italy he had learned to love through Charles Diodati. Something must be done, Milton began to feel, about his wanderlust.

In 1637, his mother died. The stricken father again fell into doubts and fears about the future of his brilliant son. Once more the question of a career was raised. But this time John was ready to lay his cards frankly upon the table and admit his literary intentions.

"Boy," old John Milton said a little plaintively, "I am as ready as the next to pay a tribute to your verses. But surely you must find a vocation other than poetry."

"It is wrong, Father, if you will let me say so, to think of poetry as a leisured sport. I am determined that I am a poet and wholly a poet. I claim that as a rich vocation."

"Hardly a vocation that will make you rich, John."

"Father, Father, don't pretend a scorn for poetry that you do not feel. You have never urged me on to some path of money-making. You have never driven me toward the bar of law or some other profession of easy, English respectability. I am yourself, Father. You have composed a thousand rich strains and to me has been given the other half of song. We have possessed the muse in shares, Father. You will not scorn me if I choose to give myself wholly over to him. I pledge you that I will be a poet to bring honor to you."

The older Milton shook his head. "I hope you won't be overproud, my boy. Don't melt your wings by too high flight, like Icarus, and fall into the sea."

"Trust me. I am not idly vain," John said, with earnest faith in the clear eyes that met his father's troubled look. "It isn't vanity for a man of force to follow the conviction God plants within him that he has a work to do. I have my own fields to plow and till in my own way. That is for me to do. The nature of the harvest is with God. Don't call my willfulness arrogance. Call it dedication."

The father shook his head. The musician had not conquered the scrivener. The honest bourgeois had not given way to the artist. Music for him had been the safe, secure sideline of the middle-class amateur. Now this son of his was launching upon that perilous sea—the profession of artist, the vocation of poet, the sculptor working with invisible air. He did not know what would come of it but he sensed the immovable will. Perhaps, secretly, it thrilled him to catch a glimpse over the mountains which his own art had been too weak to climb.

"All right, John," he said reluctantly. "You have spoken honorably and fairly. I know you are not lazy, I know you have a talent. Perhaps it will bring you true rewards. What I have to help and further you with is freely yours."

It was agreed that John should go to the Continent, to ripen in the rich soils of other cultures. But in the midst of planning and anticipation came a new event. Edward King, his friend at Cambridge, was drowned in the sinking of a ship in the Irish sea. John instantly responded when his former classmates proposed a book of commemorative poems. For this volume he

wrote the beautiful monody of *Lycidas,* one of the noblest elegies in the English language. Yet somehow, though grief and
love for the departed boy were plentifully there, the strange
prank of genius carried the poem beyond its simple purpose
and made of it a guidepost to John Milton's future.

Into *Lycidas* there crept signs that the secluded poet had
not, so much as might have been thought, forgot to notice the
growing tyranny of church and state around him. Using by
contrast the pure spirit of the departed boy, he lashed out suddenly against the grasping clergy and the corrupted church.

> Blind mouths! that scarce themselves know how to hold
> A sheep-hook, or have learned aught else the least
> That to the faithful herdsman's art belongs!
> . . . .
> The hungry sheep look up and are not fed.

He closed the poem with his own restless mood, "Tomorrow
to fresh woods and pastures new." He must be off. England
was suddenly too close and cramped for him. The air was stale.
His arrogant confidence was not blind conceit. He felt a need
to stretch and grow and learn still more. He felt the flush of
pride that the last few years had earned him. If he wrote no
more, his place among the English poets was assured. But this
was nothing. John Milton was no mere weaver of sweet pas-
torals.

Charles Diodati, now a doctor, wrote from the north of England. "What are you doing?" he demanded. So once again to
this old friend Milton spoke his true mind. "Let it be in your
private ear, lest I blush; and allow me for a little to use big language with you. You ask what I am thinking of? So may the
good Deity help me, of immortality! And what am I doing?
Growing my wings and meditating flight."

Chapter 4

"Fresh Woods and Pastures New"

Younger brother Christopher had just married and wished to enjoy some privacy with his bride at Horton. Some tedious legal affairs which had burdened the elder Milton were at last ended. Everything combined to make it an excellent moment for John's long planned continental pilgrimage.

It was April, 1638, and John, now almost thirty, came into London for his last-minute preparations. His father had backed up with a good will his final consent for the son to follow his own course in life. He equipped him with a valet and a well-laden purse. Old Henry Wotton, who had slyly urged the boy toward this goal ever since knowing him, also contributed by giving him a handful of letters to friends and acquaintances highly placed in France and Italy.

"Italy is where I truly want to go," John had always insisted. He was partly under the spell of the Mediterranean country as a result of his long friendship with Charles Diodati. The rich reminiscences of Wotton had helped to whet his appetite for this land.

Wotton chuckled and would perversely sing the praises of the French, decrying his familiar, long-loved Italy with quips and slurs. "Italy is a paradise inhabited with devils," he said. But on the eve of John's departure, the shrewd old diplomat gave him one simple piece of advice to guide his conduct in foreign lands. "Don't tell everything you know and don't say everything you think. Thoughts close, face frank."

From London to Dover, then across the rough Channel in

a bobbing shallop to Calais, thence to Paris. It was a kind of liberation and rebirth. This was a thing he had needed. A newly quickened and glowing spirit had flared in him from his first step on the European shore. He had clear purposes in mind. He would see these lands and grasp at the core of them, however swiftly it must be done. His mind was bent upon more than common sights. It would be fine to look at monumental buildings; but he also meant to look at monumental men.

He kept his eye on the main chance and refused to distract himself with small details. The tasks of finding lodgings, caring for linen, and the endless necessaries of daily living he left to his manservant. His own energies were devoted to the larger strategy.

As a beginning he sent a letter from Wotton to Michael Branthwaite, tutor to the son of Count Sligo, Charles's Ambassador to the Court of France. Then he went out to wander through the city.

He had found lodgings near the Faubourg St. Germain, where the nobility and the well-to-do of the better classes lived. His first inspection took him down along the bridges of the Seine. The Pont Neuf, the twelve-arched bridge of hewn stone with its huge, Florentine statue of Henry the Great, attracted him. By the iron grillwork around the statue he joined the cluster of idlers watching the tricks of sleight-of-hand performed by the Parisian mountebanks in the hope of a few coins.

Back along the way he had come was a panorama of the city with Notre Dame and the palace of the Louvre dominating the lesser buildings. This city of the French impressed him. It had a more open sweep than most of the cramped districts of Old London. The houses were built of finer stone, for the most part, lending the city, for all its darker quarters, a handsome appearance. Where London straggled out for miles along the Thames this city was clustered in a roughly circular form within the river valley. As he went through its lowest lying sections Milton's nose was assailed by sulphurous odors from the dirt and mud. The streets were paved chiefly with flat free-stones, square in shape, which were easier for foot and carriage than the rounded cobble-stones of London streets.

On higher ground, in the southwest quarter of the city, he found the university, and within its grounds the stalls of book-sellers. Here was sufficient goal for one day. He searched among their wares but found no special prizes.

Within a day or so he was received by Branthwaite, at the house of the Ambassador.

"I hope I can be of service to you, Mr. Milton," the tutor said, warmly. "Sir Henry speaks so highly of you as to render any-thing I may do almost a duty."

"Thank you, Mr. Branthwaite. I know you can direct me wisely in my studies of the city."

"To the best of my ability I shall try. Also, within the week, I shall arrange to present you to His Lordship. It is a pleasing privilege for him to entertain our worthy countrymen and be of assistance to them."

"Excellent."

Now there was waiting to be done, but John wasted no time. He went again to the university and inspected the noble library of the College of Navarre, then to the ancient buildings of the Sorbonne, where he gained admittance to the schools. Louis XIII was still on the throne of France, but the power in the realm was Richelieu, the shrewd cardinal. This ruthless states-man was more than a creature of intrigues and power plots. His intellect and vision had restored the decaying Sorbonne to prime condition. The Paris Milton saw was at the threshold of an era. But a few scant years and the weak king and his strong minister would both be dead, giving way to the long, fabulous regime of *Le Grand Monarque,* Louis XIV.

The meeting with the Ambassador at last came about, the first of several. Lord Scudamore, Count Sligo, was a gracious, worldly man. He played the game of ambassadorship for bigger stakes than old Wotton and had the wealth to accept the Paris post which Wotton had declined. He was willing enough to be gracious to the young man who came with no demands to make upon him. They dined together.

"Now then," the Ambassador said at length, "what can I chiefly do for you, during your stay?"

"My stay will not be long, Your Excellency," Milton explained, "for I am anxious to get on to Italy."

"You are a true protégé of Wotton," the Count observed, smiling.

"There is one thing I should like."

"Name it."

"I should like to meet Hugo Grotius."

"Ah, indeed!" Lord Scudamore stared closely at his youthful guest. This simple request had told him volumes. The lad must be of some stature himself. His intention to be on his way, coupled with this request, made it quite clear that the hope of meeting Grotius was his chief interest in Paris. It argued an uncommon mind in so young a man to recognize in the Swedish Ambassador one of the first men of his times. "You are not interested in me, my lad," Scudamore thought to himself. "I am merely the passkey to the man you wish to meet." Still, who of the many guests at the Embassy bore him any true regard? Since he must be cultivated for one motive or another this was a rather high one.

"So you would like to meet the good Grotius, eh?" he said to Milton. "How is that?"

"He is a great man," said Milton, simply.

"True. Still, if you will let an older man be impertinent with you, what have you to say to him?"

"I cannot tell you until I know what he will say to me."

The Ambassador laughed. "An honest approach," he said, appreciatively. "Tell me, why are great men always lodestones to draw young, ambitious men toward them like compass needles?"

"They are not lodestones, sir, they are whetstones. They sharpen us and make us keen."

"Very good. You are candid and persuasive, Mr. Milton. But what can this do for the great? Why should they let you use them so?"

"Well, Your Excellency, the stone that feels the young blade upon it from time to time will not decay with moss and mildew."

"The final thrust! Very well, then, Mr. Milton. I am persuaded that the excellent Grotius cannot afford to miss you. I will make arrangements."

Huig van Grot, or Hugo Grotius in the Latin form, could well capture a young man's imagination. He was of Dutch birth. His father had been a curator of the University of Leyden. Huig wrote Latin verses at nine; attended the university at twelve; and at fifteen he edited an encyclopedic work and was a member of a special embassy to France.

At a time when Holland was torn by religious conflict—as England had been and soon would be again—Grotius was an Arminian, that is, a follower of Jacobus Arminius, a critic of Calvin's doctrine of predestination. Losing the struggle, he found himself, in 1619, sentenced to life imprisonment in the Fortress of Louvenstein. His loyal wife got permission to share his imprisonment. He was permitted to have cases of books sent in to him, from time to time, which he sent out along with his linen when he was through with them and ready for a fresh batch. His wife contrived a means of escape. She persuaded him to get into the chest in which the books were carried. Two soldiers came, on schedule, to remove it and grumbled at its weight.

"There must be an Arminian in it," one of them complained.

"There are indeed Arminian books in it," Madame Grotius replied, blandly.

The chest was delivered safely to the house of the friend who handled his books for him. Grotius disguised himself as a mason, complete with hod and trowel, and managed to escape over the frontier. One of the great jurists of history, he was the father of the principle of the freedom of the seas, and author of the celebrated treatise on the natural principles of law, *De jure belli et pacis* (*The Law of War and Peace*). Now, in Paris, he was in the service of Sweden's Queen Christina as Ambassador to France.

True to his promise, the British Ambassador arranged the meeting. "I have a feeling you will not regret this interview," he assured Grotius. The great man was then fifty-five, massive and bearded. He received Milton graciously in an untidy study, littered with manuscripts, maps, and open books.

"Welcome, young man. I am glad to see you if you will pay no attention to the confusion of my room. I am not a neat, orderly scholar."

Milton smiled with enthusiasm, feeling the force of the man's personality. This was the manner of man he sought. These were the things that would be worth the trip. "You know you need not apologize, sir, for the neatness and order is within you. It is for me to apologize for the confusion of my mind."

Grotius was squinting at him sharply from his comfortable, X-shaped Italian chair. "Come," he said sharply, "let us both dispense with conventional modesties. You are no man to be puling about the confusion of your mind if you have the brazen-ness and determination to seek me out and intrude upon me. That is, unless you have done so from idle curiosity in which case I shall speed you out in short order. Come now, speak your mind!"

"That is fair, Master Grotius. I take pride in an orderly mind and am not above preening myself upon it. You wring the con-fession from me."

"Good! You appear intelligent. What are you?"

"A poet."

"God save us! I expected a fledgling lawyer, or something of the sort. I've played about with verses like all the rest, but you haven't come to me for my eminence in letters. What does a lit-erary man want with me?"

"You have half answered me, Master Grotius. The craft of poet has grounded itself in shallows if it seems astonishing for a poet to seek the company of great intellects. I am not a poet for pretty verses. I must shape a purpose for myself. I have come to Europe chiefly in search of it."

"You want to be a converting poet, eh?"

Milton hesitated over the thought. "Well, perhaps. I look upon the calling as properly a ministry, of a kind."

"What's the matter with the company of poets? Don't they have intellects?" Grotius hurled the stern sounding question with a gleam of good humor in his eyes.

"They've fallen into the way of cavaliers and courtiers. I saw little about me in England but pretty poets or narrow, con-forming clergymen."

"Clergymen? Perhaps we shall find out something. You are Protestant, of course?"

"Yes."

"Whom do you follow? The worthy Bishop Laud?"

"No, sir!" Milton vehemently rejected the assumption. "If you must call me anything, I am a Puritan."

"You don't look like one."

"Why not?" Milton asked in surprise.

"What! You aren't aware of it? You haven't the sour-pickle face for one thing, like the pickle-herring of our vulgar Dutch comedies. You groom that handsome head of hair of yours like a lure for the ladies. Your garb . . . well, it's not spectacular, but it isn't somber either. I suppose you can be a Puritan, but I hadn't thought of it."

John was slightly ruffled by the gentle mockery. "I have a Puritan mind," he said, severely.

"Oh, austere youth! I beg your pardon." Grotius laughed and got up restlessly from his chair. "Now then," he demanded, swinging in big strides about his study, "all this being the case, what the devil are you doing in Europe looking for a purpose?"

Milton was growing bewildered by the whirlwind nature of the man. "What do you mean, sir?"

"Here!" Grotius stopped beside a heavy globe and gave it a powerful spin. It rumbled heavily on its pedestal. "Look at this globe, which a few Inquisition-minded dunderheads are still none too sure about. Look at it, I say! Nowhere on all its surface can you find a better purpose of the kind you're looking for than back in England. If that's what you want, cancel your plans and hurry back there. Don't spend another night talking to ambassadors or the like. Go home."

"No, sir, I won't. I came abroad for a purpose and I mean to stay here, unless you give me particulars."

"Now we speak of other purposes. Well, don't take me too seriously. You're quite right. Stay here, or wherever it is you're going. But mark what I said. If you want to find anything for this ministry of yours you'll find it at home. Maybe this trip will teach you that. As for particulars, I won't give them. Find them out for yourself. You're the Englishman, I'm not."

"I thought," Milton said earnestly, speaking as though to the friend of a lifetime, "that I must find the roots of an epic somewhere in my own English culture. To see it best I thought a plunge into the cultures of other nations might help. I've been thinking a little about the possibility of a long poem on the Arthurian legend; not romances, but a study of English freedom in thought and worship."

"Don't try to study English freedom in a kingly theme, boy," Grotius said.

"That's not impossible," Milton insisted.

"It may not be impossible, but with a heavy hand such as Charles's upon the throne it will not seem a fortunate choice. But enough of this. I don't want to debate with you. Where are you going from here?"

"Now that I have met you, to Italy, I think."

"What do you hope to find in the shadow of the popes and the Inquisition?"

"There are great spirits there," Milton affirmed, stubbornly.

"Yes, there are, some of them," Grotius admitted. "Don't let me seem intolerant. There is one in particular, Galileo Galilei."

Milton leapt at the name. The old astronomer was the man he would most like to see in all Europe. "Galileo! Do you know him?"

Grotius nodded, sadly. "Yes, I saw him, not so very long ago. He was beginning to fail. The Inquisition has him, now."

"Galileo!" Milton was preoccupied and had hardly heard the last words. "Do you think, by any means, it would be possible to see him?"

Grotius stared at his visitor. "You are ambitious, aren't you? No, Milton, it seems unlikely. Here, let me show you. . . ."

He interrupted himself and went to the big table to rummage in the piles of papers on it. "I have a letter here," he went on, as he searched, "from Galileo, sent over to me a few days ago by our friend Elia Diodati, who received it."

"Diodati!"

"Yes, why are you so surprised?"

"It is the name of my dearest friend, a nephew of Dr. John Diodati of Geneva. It could not be the same?"

"No, but the same family. They are a famous tribe. Now then, here. . . ." He sat down again, with a letter in his hand. "This will tell you how matters stand with the poor fellow. 'Your dear friend and servant, Galileo, has been for the last month perfectly blind, so that this heaven, this earth, this universe, which I by my marvelous discoveries and clear demonstrations have enlarged a hundred thousand times beyond the belief of the wise men of bygone years, henceforward is for me shrunk into such a small space as is filled by my own bodily sensations. So it pleases God; so also shall it therefore please me.' "

Both men were silent for a moment. "So you see," said Grotius, finally, "he is in poor sorts to receive the homage of visitors. He is in his villa near Florence, closely watched. The Pope thinks his ideas dangerous."

"Nevertheless," said Milton, with the spark of purpose in his eye, "I shall try what I can do."

"Do so, then. I wish you luck. Should you get to him, extend my love and brotherhood. Use my name in any way you choose, if it will aid you."

These two men, the young poet and the mature statesman, had struck a kinship. As Milton rose to go Grotius embraced him warmly and led him to the door. "I am glad you came, Milton. We are friends. Send me your poems." Then, on an afterthought, as the young man disappeared down the hall, he called after him, "And by the way, just for fair exchange, I will send you my *Adamus exul,* you'll find it a pretentious sort of piece, about the Fall of Man."

It was evening as Milton came out upon the streets of Paris. The air was that of a beautiful June night but to John it was unlike the air he had breathed an hour earlier. The personality of Grotius had been, to him, like an added oxygen content. He breathed a heady air and the Puritan mind swam a little as he walked down by the Seine and gazed absently at the dark, gleaming ripples of the river by night.

"Well," demanded Lord Scudamore when he next chanced upon Grotius at the palace, "what did you think of my young countryman? He's left for Italy in the meantime."

"Yes," said Grotius, "he wants to meet Galileo."

The English Ambassador roared with laughter, drawing puzzled stares from those near by. "So," he cried, "you, too, Grotius, are just another station on the relay. I am comforted. He sought me out to get at you. Now it seems he sought you out to get at Galileo! Whom does he expect Galileo to present him to? As an expert on the heavens, perhaps to God!"

Grotius shrugged good-humoredly. Let the Englishman enjoy his joke. He knew the truth.

By way of Nice, Genoa, Pisa, and Leghorn, Milton finally reached the city of Florence, early in August. The Italy he had been eagerly awaiting had already firmly fixed its spell upon him with its richness of sights and associations, and the lushness of the Mediterranean summer. Now the great city of the Medici enthralled him. It nestled at the foot of the Apennines, under the deep blue Italian skies, richly set about with fruitful groves and green meadows. The broad and shallow Arno coursed through its midst and wherever one looked the eye fell upon beauty.

John passed, as he entered the city, the portico of the Palazzo Vecchio where, at close quarters, were to be seen the David of Michelangelo and the copper Perseus of Benvenuto Cellini. The treasures of the city were inexhaustible. He stayed through August and September, frequenting the great spectacles of art and architecture, haunting the library of the Church of San Lorenzo, and making friends with the young men of the Florentine academies.

If Milton had adopted Italy, then that gracious country likewise adopted him. He had arrived with a sheaf of introductions, but was his own best pass of entry. The young poets and intellectuals of Florence took him to themselves. He ate and drank with them, took part in the sessions of their informal academies, the *Vogliati* and the *Apasti,* where he recited his verses in Latin, Italian, French, and English, astonishing them with his command of languages. The withdrawn Puritan of Cambridge had melted utterly into his Italian environment. He bewildered his friends with his vigorous enthusiasm, his versatile talents, his graciousness. They called him "the noble Inglese." What captured him here, in contrast to the idle wastrels of Cambridge with their bear-baiting and tedious pastimes, was the deep-drawn, passionate, probing love for life. He thought himself half an Italian.

For their part, his new-found friends adored him. The youngest and closest of them, Carolo Dati, was merely eighteen but possessed the brilliance and maturity of manhood. Benedetto Bonmattei, Pietro Frescobaldi, Jacopo Gaddi who had a rare collection of art objects, all viewed him with a wondering respect. The people of England may have failed to realize, or seen dimly, what was in their midst. But surely this was a case of the prophet unhonored in his own country. These freeminded Italians did not doubt for a moment that a great man walked among them. The goals of his high mission which were set up in his mind, to which he made partial confession among these responsive friends, seemed to them the natural and inevitable future for one so gifted. Milton basked in praise and appreciation.

Outside the limits of the city he had seen Arcetri, the villa of Galileo. He had not forgotten his desire to meet this titan. But it seemed unattainable. By everyone the suggestion was received as a shocking impossibility. He was advised to forget it and leave well enough alone.

October found him in Rome. More quickly even than before, he was engulfed in the making of new friends, the attractions of new sights and enterprises. Here, too, he was drawn into the academies and literary clubs.

It was natural that this Puritan mind should take pause at finding itself in the seat and fountainhead of Papacy. True, all Italy was Catholic. Milton had seldom touched upon the theme with his Florentine friends. But here, in the shadow of the Vatican, he could not wholly check himself after the wise advice of Wotton.

He made the rounds of the great churches of the city. Their beauty and majesty stirred him as much as anyone. But his Puritan mind was oppressed and revolted by what seemed to him a display of sham and superstition. At the Lateran Church of St. John were two columns of the veil of the Temple of Jerusalem, the stone with which lots were cast for Christ's garments, the pillar upon which the cock crowed when Peter denied Christ, and the foot measurements of the Virgin Mary as supplied by her shoemaker. They boasted also a flat stone raised on four pillars which was said to be the exact height of Jesus. No man would match it, but would be found to be a bit taller or a bit shorter.

St. Peter's, crowded with visitors come to celebrate its completion, boasted the miraculous veil of Veronica whereon the face of Christ was printed. In other churches were to be seen part of the crib in which the Babe lay at Bethlehem, a bloody stump whereon the Saviour was scourged, and a pillar to which St. Paul was bound when his head was cut off. This pillar had taken three great leaps, when the deed was done, leaving a fountain flowing after each leap.

These, and the countless other spectacles, seemed to Milton a ghastly, religious sideshow. He ventured to express himself a little on the subject, entering into discussions of religion with a few of his friends with the frankness of a man bred to liberty.

In the burial chapels beneath St. Peter's he had gazed with interest at the tomb of the English pope, Adrian IV, born Nicholas Breakspear. He went to the church of the English Jesuits and talked with them.

His chief friend in Rome was the librarian of the Vatican, Lucas Holstenius, who laid before him the rare treasures in his keeping; two parchment manuscripts of Virgil, one of Terence, the Acts of the Apostles in golden letters, the epigrams of Petrarch in his own handwriting.

Through Holstenius he was introduced to the Cardinal Francesco Barberini, nephew of the Pope. This dignitary took a tolerant liking to the young Protestant and invited him to a musical entertainment of great magnificence at his palace. The feature of the evening was the singing of Leonora Baroni, the foremost singer of her day.

Milton, versed in music and well able to admire the glories of this voice, was carried quite beyond himself and fell instantly in love with the beautiful Leonora. Suddenly his perspective of Rome and Italy was dizzily altered. The well-balanced head of which he had boasted to Grotius was spinning.

The weeks that followed were absorbed for him in thoughts of his dark-haired queen of song. She was twenty-seven, now, and in her prime. That half the eminent men of Italy stumbled over one another to get at her, made no jot of difference to the amazing Puritan. He poured his gift of song out to her in Latin and Italian verses. In the houses of his highly connected friends he encountered her frequently and pressed his courtship. Alas, what was a pale young Puritan, handsome though he was, in this ripe era of gorgeous Rome? She was tolerant and friendly to him, as what fair woman is not to a worthy suitor. But he was shut out, banned as anything other than a new Laureate, to sing her praises for awhile, in her native tongue, more eloquently than her fellow countrymen. He made a minor nuisance of himself to friendly patrons by praising her to whom they, too, were addressing poems, or even extolling her unwittingly to those who had known her favors. No progress was made. He gave it up, sadly.

Down to Naples he went, late in November, to forget everything. Here he met the eminent and aged Marquis of Villa, Giovanni Battista Manso. The old gentleman was a poet himself and the founder of an academy. He had been the patron of the great Torquato Tasso.

Manso liked Milton, and in his old-worldliness found him naïve. He took pleasure in conducting him about Naples during part of his stay. But Milton was becoming a little too outspoken on religious subjects. Certain of his friends felt they could not afford to see too much of him. Manso was one of these and frankly admitted it. Some time later he sent Milton a handsome gift of engraved cups together with the lines:

Joannes Baptista Mansus, Marquis of Villa,
Neopolitan, to John Milton, Englishman.
Mind, form, grace, face, and morals are perfect; if but thy
  creed were,
Then not Anglic alone, truly angelic thou'dst be.

John had planned to go from Naples to Sicily and Greece. But disturbing rumors of civil war in England reached him. If this were true it was hardly fitting for him to continue his travels as a gentleman of leisure. At the same time, certain persons told him that the English Jesuits of Rome, angered at his outspoken Protestant opinions, were hatching a plot against him, were he to return.

This was meat and drink to Milton, whose mood it suited to take it seriously. He hastened back to Rome in mid-winter. Here the word from England was such that he felt he need not hurry overmuch. It would be enough to refrain from traveling further. There was still much to see and do. He remained nearly two months more. As for the Jesuits, whatever the case may have been he did not find them lurking at corners with stilettos. There was some hostility and certain persons had cooled toward him. More than any other thing, his open Protestantism had gone far to wear out his welcome.

Toward the end of February he began his homeward steps by returning to Florence. Here he had entered no religious disputes and determined not to do so. His old friends greeted him warmly and took him back into their circles.

Though now he understood more clearly the difficulties in his way he was still bent upon seeing Galileo. Finally Antonio Francini said to him, "Speak to Malatesti. He knows the old man."

Antonio Malatesti was a bawdy, witty poet who had lavished upon the English Puritan reams of risqué poems. He was one to whom John had never directly mentioned the question of Galileo. Now Milton put the problem before his friend.

"All right," said Malatesti, "there is no guarantee of success but you may succeed if you are willing to brazen it out."

"I'll try."

"I've watched things at Arcetri. They say His Holiness has

relented a little. There are two steps to it: first you must get them to tell the old man you are there, that is where my name may be useful. Then send word that I sent you. He will probably refuse to see you, for I am no special friend of his, though he knows me. Then send word that you bring him greetings from Grotius. If that does no good, give it up."

The following day, about noon, Milton mounted his horse and rode the few miles to the Villa Arcetri. Here was cloistered one of the greatest minds of Europe because Pope Urban VIII and his Inquisition feared the undermining of the church by his heretical opinions that the earth moved around the sun and not the sun around the earth. A scientific heresy so great seemed as dangerous as Protestantism. Vivid in Milton's memory was the burden of the recantation which had been wrung from Galileo and which the church had diligently published throughout the world:

". . . Because I have been enjoined by this Holy Office altogether to abandon the false opinion which maintains that the sun is the center and immovable, and forbidden to hold, defend, or teach the said false doctrine in any manner, and after it had been signified to me that the said doctrine is repugnant with the Holy Scripture. . . . I abjure, curse, and detest the said heresies and errors . . . and I swear that I will never more in future say or assert anything verbally, or in writing, which may give rise to a similar suspicion of me."

John dismounted and approached the gate of the villa. He knocked and was greeted by a servant.

"I have come to see Messer Galilei."

"Do you come by authority?"

"No, by my own initiative."

"Are you known to him?"

"No, I am a stranger, from England, seeking to greet him with my respect."

"It is impossible. Messer Galilei is not to be disturbed."

"I am sent by Antonio Malatesti, of Florence, who is known to you."

"It is impossible."

"At least announce me. I am John Milton, of England, sent by Antonio Malatesti."

"I cannot."

Half fearful of a blunder, but as a last resort, Milton drew out a gold coin and put it into the servant's hand. After all, he was a sort of guard, in all likelihood.

"Please announce me."

The man disappeared. After a long wait he reappeared. "He will not see you," he said. "He begs to be excused."

"Did you really announce me?"

"Yes, signor."

"Then please report once more. Tell him that I bear him greetings from Hugo Grotius, in Paris."

Accepting another coin the servant disappeared within once more. Returning at length he said, "It is very unusual. He will receive you."

Milton's heart leapt. Eagerly he followed his guide into the dark rooms of the villa. He was led into a spacious study. Seated in the center of it was the old, white-bearded astronomer. He looked weak and ill and unhappy. His eyes were closed.

"I cannot see you, Messer Miltone," he said in a gentle voice as he heard him enter, "will you be good enough to come near me?" Messer "Miltone" he called him, rounding and stretching the "o" as though an "e" were added to the name.

Milton advanced to the blind man and bent over, kissing his hand. "Thank you for your graciousness in receiving me, Messer Galilei. If it meant less than a great deal to me I could not have presumed so much."

"Sit down," Galileo directed, speaking quietly. There was an

Italian stool close by. Milton seated himself upon it. "Why have you come to see me?"

"First, to bring you greetings of brotherhood from Hugo Grotius, with whom I talked in Paris some months ago."

"Ah, yes, Grotius. He is one of our great, although a Protestant. Is he well?"

"Well, indeed," said Milton, "and much busied with affairs of state for Her Majesty of Sweden. He grieves to hear of your blindness."

"Thank him for me," said Galileo. "Tell him there is no thing more useless than a blind astronomer, but that it matters little for I am no longer an astronomer."

"Then further, Messer Galilei, I have come to offer you my homage. There is no bold man in Europe who does not venerate you. I am not a scientist, but I love truth and I have read astronomy. I believe your system of the universe."

"I have no system of the universe," the old man said gently. *". . . And I swear that I will never more in future say or assert anything, verbally or in writing . . ."*

"Nevertheless," said Milton, after a moment, "I believe in it."

"You are English, you said. And I suppose you are Protestant?"

"Yes."

"It is not the best thing for me to receive Protestants. You must understand, young sir, that you are talking with a prisoner. It is an informal bondage but no less firm. It is not openly declared such but it is admitted between me and my jailers."

"I hope my visit will do you no injury."

"No, I have behaved well and they are more lenient. Besides, you are not a scientist. What, then, are you?"

"I am a poet."

"Ah, very good. You have somewhat to do with stars, then.

And poets, also, are a dangerous sort of men. But you can create such a heaven as you see fit without fear of consequences. You called yourself, by inclusion, a bold man. Why so?"

"I, too, am something of a heretic."

"But you are fortunate. You live in a Protestant kingdom. There is no pope, there is no Inquisition."

Surprising patterns of thought were shaping clearly in Milton's mind. New forms appeared in familiar things. He followed his swift thoughts aloud.

"We have pope and Inquisition in our own way. Are you acquainted with the state of things in England?"

"No. I hear of little outside these walls."

"We have a sort of pope of the Church of England, whom we call Archbishop. We have an Inquisition of the Church and Court which we call Star Chamber. And also we have a king who has shown himself daily more of a tyrant. So I shall hasten back to England which is threatened with civil war."

"This is strange," said Galileo. "And what are you in this?"

"I am a Protestant within Protestantism. I must take my side in a new reformation against the Reformation. We are split many ways, but I call myself Puritan."

"Puritan," repeated Galileo. "It is a noble word. I like it."

"So you will see," said Milton, "that there is some reason for me to be drawn to you. Perhaps I must, myself, face an ordeal. I need all the wisdom I can gather."

Galileo meditated for some moments while Milton stared at the worn, noble face. "Of course, I am a Catholic," he said at last. "It is the faith in which I was nurtured and it would be idle for me to profess another religion because of the troubles my science has brought me to. What you say to me of England makes this more clear. And I have heard things of the rule of Calvin at Geneva that were the same.

"I could incline with friendship toward Protestantism because in many of my learned and great-souled friends it has looked forward more freely than the church. But I am neither fanatical Papist nor Protestant, in fact. It was because of this that I could recant. What, after all, was the church form to me? They know I am right. They need time to stretch their theology to the new frame I have given it. Very well, let them have time."

This, Milton felt, was an apology. He accepted it. The old astronomer had yielded and spoken honestly with him. He was honored. Looking into the pain-scarred face he wanted to ask, *"Did your denial set back the progress of your science?"* This seemed suddenly of such importance to him. Someday he too might suffer a reversal.

"Do you think the truth can die?" John asked.

Galileo turned his sightless eyes toward him. He understood the question. "No," he said, "I think it cannot. We make a truth our own when we, alone, have sought it out. It remains our own while it is undisclosed. But once we have let it out it is released and cannot become again the captive of one man. We can then deny it and abuse it, if we wish, like a father casting off a wayward son who has brought grief to him, but it is beyond our harming. It lives for itself. If this were not so we could not stand our weaknesses."

Milton arose and again kissed the hand of the blind man. "I tire you," he said, affectionately. "You have rewarded me handsomely for my journey. I shall always remember you."

Galileo rose painfully from his chair but did not try to move away from it. He reached out and grasped Milton's shoulder. "I do not receive many people," he said, "but I am glad that you came to me. You have a vision. I hope it will be faithful to you; I know you will to it. Good-by, Messer Miltone. God go with you."

Out into the sunlight John went, from the gloom of the villa.

He mounted his horse and rode slowly back toward Florence. This meeting, of all things in his long pilgrimage, he would tell with pride in later days. He knew that he had met one who measured up to fullness and overflowing to the standard he had once defined as a goal for man, one "such as to have even once seen shall be boasted of by others as something meritorious."

Some days after, John visited the Church of the Annunciata to see certain masterworks of Andrea del Sarto. His companion drew him aside into a chapel to see a painting by one Bartolomeo which had, with it, a legend. It was said that the artist completed the figure of the Virgin, all but the face which, unable to do justice to it, he left blank, intending to attempt it the following day. When he returned to his work in the morning, according to the legend, he drew aside the cloth and found a glowing and inspired countenance painted by a miraculous hand. The picture was now concealed always within a cabinet and visited by thousands, for it was reputed to have miraculous powers.

"Look well upon it, my friend," said Valerio Clementillo, who was with him, "for those who have beheld this face will never lose their sight."

Milton gazed upon it thoughtfuly. *"Galileo should have seen it,"* he was thinking.

Reluctantly Milton began to shape his course toward home. He stopped off for a little time in Venice, and from the city of canals shipped home to England an assortment of books, music, and manuscripts he had gathered along the stages of his journey. Finally he crossed the Alps to Switzerland and spent two weeks in Geneva, the world seat of Protestantism.

Here a blow awaited him. From the great preacher, Dr. John Diodati, he learned that his friend and confidant Charles had died in August, 1638. The letter Milton had written him from Rome, singing the beauties of Leonora Baroni, had been addressed to a dead man.

This, and the news of gathering storms in England, all but crushed the greater part of the joy out of him. Only the sustaining light of his rich experiences and associations, the inspiration of his meetings with Grotius and Galileo, upheld his spirit.

For his brief stay in the Lake city he took daily comfort in talks with Dr. Diodati and in listening to this learned preacher's sermons. All things pointed to a crisis in England over religious freedom and Charles's ambition to rule unchecked. Dr. Diodati was grave about it. Milton's thoughts were shaping. The career of poet might suffer some delay. Grotius and Galileo had broadly pointed him toward home in their separate ways. The pilgrimage was over. He would go, now, and take up the challenge at his own threshold.

Chapter 5

The Sabbath Men

IN THE HEAT of an August day the heavy coach from Dover rumbled into London, jammed with passengers. The long stage between the great city and the channel port was choked with travelers in both directions. There were troubles in England. Back from the Continent were streaming one sort of travelers, drawn back by the strife at home. There was the opposing traffic of those of a certain position and leisure who were hastening off to be free of the unpleasantness. These were relatively few. It was the firm wish not to be classed with them that had turned Milton's course homeward when the earliest rumors had reached him.

Once again in the familiar Bread Street neighborhood, travel-stained and wearied, Milton got down from the coach. He walked to the sign of the spread eagle and paid his respects to his father's partner in the scrivener's shop.

"The old gentleman is in the country, Master John," he was told. "Won't you lodge here until you're settled?"

"Perhaps, thank you," John said, "at least for this night. There are bad times afoot, I hear."

Every Londoner seemed a talking spigot, waiting to be turned on. "Lord save England, Master John! Trouble is right. The Earl of Strafford and Bishop Laud between 'em will whisk us back to Rome before we know we've even got to Dover! The Scots won't have it and no more will people here, I hope!"

"Bad, bad," John agreed, and begged off from more. There were things he must do.

The city buzzed and seethed. On the trip from Dover he had heard the facts of the situation that had been rumored in Naples. King Charles had mismanaged affairs between England and Scotland. The religious pattern of Scotland was complicated enough in itself, for the country was divided between Roman Catholics, whose faith was persecuted, and Presbyterians. Now, in 1639, the King and Archbishop Laud attempted to force upon officially Protestant Scotland a revised Prayer Book. To the militant Presbyterians this Church of England form of worship was "Popish" and in Edinburgh angry shouts were heard of "The Mass is entered amongst us!" There was always sentiment for Scottish nationalism. With this inflamed by the religious issue, King Charles Stuart, of the very Scottish line that had united the thrones of Scotland and England, now found himself at war with Scotland.

Charles had neither enough money nor enough men to crush Scotland and was quickly made to face the fact. The first skirmishes had shown his weakness and he had backed down hastily to bide his time again. If there had been no real war as yet it was not the King's fault. Now he was seeking the means to arm himself and begin all over.

John's mind was fixed first upon another matter. He went out to the neighborhood of Aldersgate Street to the house of Dr. Diodati, father of his dead friend. It was a year, now, since Charles Diodati had died, but at the sight of Milton, tears forced themselves into the old physician's eyes. John's throat was choked with his own feeling. The old man and the young one embraced silently in their common grief.

Dr. Diodati gained possession of himself. "Welcome, John, welcome! In spite of an old man's weak tears it gladdens me to see you. You bring something of Charles to me."

"I have been back little more than an hour and hasted to seek you out, to find someone whose loss was as great as mine, or greater. I journeyed with its weight on my heart the whole way from Geneva."

"I comfort myself only that it was the way of his choice," the doctor said. "He entered a profession that walks often in the valley of the shadow. It has taken him and spared me. That is my only reproach."

"Tell me about it. I know nothing."

Dr. Diodati sighed. "The plague, the plague—the Black Death. We physicians are as helpless in the face of it as the lowliest chimney sweep. I warned him of it; warned him there was nothing he could do. But he said if he was a healer of sicknesses he would acquaint himself with them. He went into Blackfriars, where the plague was raging, and was swept off with it. He was buried there, as the plague dead must be."

"The loss is everlasting for me," John said. "To whom shall I confide myself? He was my dearest friend."

"I have found that it is God's meaning, when He takes our props away from us, that we should stand alone," the older man said. "Now there are things to be done here that will help us all forget our griefs. You visited my brother in Geneva?"

"Yes."

"There is a crisis for Protestants here," the doctor said. "If they go on this way, things will draw close to the conditions that made Protestants like myself abandon Italy. And the worst is that it is not Papists but other Protestants that make the trouble."

"I have talked about it not only with your brother, but with Grotius and Galileo," Milton said. "When the rumors of struggle here began to reach me I headed homeward. I must look about now and find what there is for me to do."

Next morning John set forth upon the search for lodgings. Stored for him in Bread Street were the cases of books and other treasures he had shipped from Venice. He must find a place where he could arrange his library, begin the tasks that would lie before him, and also, without failing in his higher purpose, find the means to earn his living. It would not do to rest wholly on the support of his father now that his period of thought and travel was done.

At the foot of Fleet Street, by St. Bride's Churchyard, was the shop of a tailor named Russell. In its window a placard proclaimed that there were rooms to let above the shop. John stood in the street and glanced upward. The empty windows on the second floor gave hint of space enough, at least. The house was old and dingy, but the street was more open than many, thanks to St. Bride's, and the choice might not be bad, for the present. It would not be expensive for this was not a select neighborhood.

He stepped into the shop. The tailor rose from his bench and came toward him, thrusting a large needle into the pouch of his apron.

"Now, sir, a suit of clothes for you? A fine coat, perhaps?"

"No, good sir," Milton replied, "I am here to ask about your rooms above stairs."

"Ha! The chambers, is it?" The tailor set his hands to his hips and stared fiercely at the young stranger. "What is your name, sir?"

"John Milton, gentleman."

"That I see, that I see. A tailor should know a gentleman, shouldn't he?" Honest Russell's manner remained stern. "You are no Papist, I hope?"

"No."

"Nor no High Churchman of any order?"

"No," said John again, amused somewhat. "I call myself a Puritan."

"Well enough, sir. We are Independents here, Mr. Milton, and we want no Papists or prelatists."

"I am none of those," Milton said. "I am a simple scholar."

"Well enough, so it is," Russell repeated, becoming friendly and breaking into a smile. "You are a seemly enough lad to be a courtier, barking and frisking around the heels of Charles. But an honest scholar is welcome here. You may have the rooms."

Now Milton smiled. "Thank you," he said. "Perhaps it would be best to see them first."

The big, hearty tailor called his wife into the shop to mind its business and led Milton to the separate entrance to the upper rooms. They were disappointing, being not so large as he had hoped; two of a fair size and one small, at the rear. They were dark, except for the one that looked upon the street, and low ceilinged. But this was so of most houses in London. The price was modest. It would do.

The weeks that followed were a turmoil. John moved his belongings into the new lodgings, buying simple furniture, laboring into the night arranging his growing store of books upon their new shelves, setting in order the musical manuscripts and the great pile of his own papers, writings and notebooks. In the midst of this there were his old friends to see; Harry Lawes, Alexander Gill, Sir Henry Wotton, and others. With them he talked of his travels and heard more stories of the bad state of England. His father had come in from Horton, rejoicing to see his son and hearing with pride the account of his triumphs in Italy.

When the excitements of homecoming had ended, he acquired a young boarder. His sister Anne had been married to one Edward Phillips, who had died in 1631, leaving her with two small boys. She had since remarried. Now she was concerned for the education of her sons. Where could she find a better tutor than her learned brother John? She made financial arrangements with him and, while Milton was yet at St. Bride's, the younger of the boys, John Phillips, aged nine, came to live and study with his uncle.

It seemed to John that he was no sooner settled in the tailor's house than it was time to move again. Christopher Milton and his wife had gone to live at Reading. His father could not live alone at Horton. There was another Phillips boy to come and all this could not be managed in the three dark rooms over the tailor shop. So, after about six months there, John moved from St. Bride's, early in 1640, into a pleasant garden house not far from Dr. Diodati in Aldersgate Street, outside the city wall. Ten-year-old Edward Phillips joined his brother and aging Father Milton moved into the household. It had become an establishment.

The morning was occupied in teaching. Not only the Phillips boys were pupils of Milton. A group of students had gathered, some of them sons of his friends, others simply the sons of wealthy or noble families who respected his scholarship. The house became a small private school.

John Milton was profoundly troubled in his heart. He was thirty-one years old. Day by day, notes and suggestions for some epic poem were creeping into the pages of his commonplace book. His genius was restless and urged him to give all his energies to the creation of the epic visions that were forming in his mind. But the world would not allow this, and John was not one who could close himself off from the world he lived in.

Liberty was much reduced in England and John loved liberty as much as poetry. If liberty had been suppressed, then he must be a part of the struggle to restore it. How this had come to pass, how it was to be remedied, and what it was that he himself must do were questions to which he must find answers. He set himself to solve them.

A tyranny existed in England. Charles I was its keystone. His strong aides, Thomas Wentworth, Earl of Strafford, and William Laud, Archbishop of Canterbury, were its pillars. Oppressive taxes were imposed by the King who needed money for an army to enforce his will. Opponents of the King could be seized without warrant, flung into prison without trial, there to be forgotten, mutilated, tortured, or executed. Two powerful bodies, England's equivalents to the Inquisition in Spain and Italy, the secret Star Chamber in politics and the High Commission in religious matters, held sway over Englishmen. English liberty had come to one of the crises of its history.

King Charles was determined to exercise absolute rule, and moved toward this with more force of character than his father, James I, had done. "I owe the account of my actions to God alone," he declared. As a divinely sanctioned monarch who felt he could do no wrong, he would stop at nothing, by the peculiar logic of that belief. A man of honesty and integrity by his own lights, he was to others a man who would make promises and break them, or lie to them openly, in the struggle for power. A series of Parliaments rebuked and opposed him, and he used his royal power to dissolve each of them. From 1629 to 1640 there had been no Parliament at all, the longest such period in more than three centuries.

Tyranny needs a strong army. Armies are expensive. The taxes imposed by the King stirred up increasing rebelliousness, and there he ran into a problem. Legally, only a Parliament, of its own will, could impose the taxes to raise the needed money. After the eleven-year lapse, Charles summoned the Houses. Instead of voting money for his army they passed resolutions of censure against him. In fury, he dissolved them.

But his needs remained. Again he convened a Parliament. This one took him by surprise. It passed a law asserting that it could not be dissolved except by its own vote. This was the famous Long Parliament. Exasperated anti-royalists were ready for anything. The Parliament flung both the Earl of Strafford and Archbishop Laud into the Tower of London, England's centuries-old political prison.

It was at about this stage of affairs that Milton found himself drawn into the struggle. His chief interest was in religious freedom. To the King, the rule of bishops over the Church was a corollary to a monarch's divine right to rule men in everything. The unanimity between the Church of England and the King gave strength to both.

The history of religious strife and persecution is a long, melancholy record that has seen many patterns within Christendom alone: Protestants persecuted by Roman Catholics, Roman Catholics persecuted by Protestants, Protestants persecuted by fellow Protestants of different sects.

The Church of England, still Catholic in its theology, was Protestant only insofar as that word is taken to mean that it had rejected the authority of the Pope—a circumstance that had come about through political considerations under the reign of Henry VIII, which resulted in more religious struggles and martyrdoms.

There are complicated but important distinctions here. The Church of England, then and now, and in America the Episcopal Church which forms part of the world-wide Anglican Communion, are technically in schism—that is, separated by organizational disagreements—from the Church of Rome. Though indeed there are now some differences in doctrine and worship these are not nearly so great as what separates theologically four Communions—Roman Catholic, Eastern Orthodox,

Old Catholic, and Anglican—from such truly Protestant bodies as Presbyterians, Lutherans, Methodists, Baptists, and a great number of others.

There are many variations of liturgy, or form of worship, within the Church of England and its American Episcopal affiliate. These are often called "low" or "high" church as indicating degrees of elaborateness of forms of worship. Events of history have given them undue importance. Low or high in form, this Church is "Protestant" only as that word is used popularly to mean, separated from Rome.

That is why, long before the lifetime of Milton, even before Shakespeare, there had been various groups of dissenters, or nonconformists, in religion who regarded the theologically-Catholic Church of England as no better than the Church of Rome and just as oppressive. In the time of King James some religious "separatists" left England and settled in Holland, but this was a land of foreign tongue, however friendly. In 1620 one band of them set forth boldly for the New World of the west and established Plymouth Plantation and the other settlements of New England. Any hardship was a fair price for freedom of worship. Since then, under Charles, thousands of strong-minded Englishmen had sold their homes and goods and sought a perilous foothold in Massachusetts or elsewhere in North America. These included Quakers in Pennsylvania and Roman Catholics in Maryland. In the Massachusetts settlements, in the way of human nature, they generated further religious disputes and oppressions among themselves; for most of us, when we talk about freedom mean *our* way. Those Protestant rebels against the Church of England, whether at home or in the New World, are rather loosely known to us as Puritans, but what lies behind the term is complicated.

Some Puritans, such as Milton, originally had been no more than members of the Church of England who condemned what they felt to be corruptions within the church, self-seeking and tyranny on the part of bishops and archbishops. They had no particular quarrel with forms of worship, nor any particular objection to bishops, who had been part of the structure of the Church from New Testament times. But they emphasized the personal aspect of the relationship between a man and God and did not believe that forms of worship, or uniform books of prayer, should be forced upon worshippers.

As conflicts increased and persecution followed, many Puritans became more extreme. The term became a catchall for many sects who had little in common except their opposition to prelacy, the rule by bishops. They included Presbyterians, Baptists, Independents or Congregationalists, Quakers, and still smaller groups such as Lollards, Hussites, and Brownists. All such, having scant love for one another, were willing to unite against Episcopal rule, another term for the authority of bishops.

Many of these Puritans were themselves as harsh and bigoted as anyone opposed to them. Many—not all—were narrow and severe in their moral codes and denounced all that they called worldly: music, dancing, gay-colored clothing, wine, theatres, and all books but those of their own theological views. Not necessarily the friends of Il Penseroso, the Meditative Man, they were definitely the enemies of L'Allegro, the Cheerful Man. They condemned utterly his "unreprovèd pleasures free. . . ." In Shakespeare's time he had allowed his pleasure-loving Sir Toby Belch, in *Twelfth Night,* to make a classic retort to a Puritan: "Dost thou think, because thou art virtuous, there shall be no more cakes and ale?" There is much about the Puritans that is unattractive, and much that is admirable. The tragedy of England's religious civil war was the familiar one that men of courage and honest conviction strove against each other.

The sterner Puritans were denounced by the royalist side for their drab dress, sour faces, and excessive self-righteousness. Each one imagined himself a battleground between God and the Devil, his own soul the prize. Good men, some of them, but humorless and harsh. They were Sabbath men to whom each month of the twelve was a month of Sundays.

Now, while Parliament held the upper hand, the religious quarrel became the King's chief hope of regaining his power. There were three views. The High Churchmen were for prelacy. A second group was for a more modified and liberal prelacy with the powers of the bishops curbed. Then there were those who wished to destroy prelacy, "root and branch."

Parliament was debating just such a "root and branch" measure against the bishops when a little pamphlet, mild in tone but firm, was put on sale at the Sign of the Pied Bull, in St. Paul's Churchyard. It was called *An Humble Remonstrance to the High Court of Parliament by a Dutiful Son of the Church*. Its author was the scholarly Bishop of Exeter, Joseph Hall. It was a manifesto of prelacy and cautioned Parliament against any attempt at checking the authority of bishops.

John had many friends in the rebellious camp. His upbringing, his Cambridge days, and all the trend of his thought since then had led him in this direction. He had drawn close, again, to Thomas Young, chief of the tutors of his boyhood studies. The clergyman had led Milton into the circles of the active fight. His youthful powers were not to be let slip in the battle for free worship.

As John was completing his morning classes with the houseful of pupils, he received a visit from Dr. Young, whose face bore witness to a serious errand.

Hastily the young schoolmaster sent the boys into the garden and confided them to the care of his father, who was sunning himself there.

"Dr. Young, it is good to see you!" Milton exclaimed as he settled down with his visitor.

"I want to enlist your services." Dr. Young drew from the inner recesses of his great Puritan coat a rolled manuscript and laid it upon the table.

"Now then," Milton said, laughing, "have you come to me with verses?"

"No, no," Dr. Young said, jutting out his lower lip and viewing the young man gravely, "quite another matter than verses, I am afraid. Have you read Bishop Hall's '*Humble Remonstrance*'?"

"Yes, I have. It is here somewhere; in the fire if it were in its right place."

Dr. Young nodded. "Quite so. Well, it must be answered, and a group of us have prepared a reply, urging the necessity for action, sharp action, root and branch!"

"A group of you?"

"Five of us, to be precise; all clergymen and all known to you. Stephen Marshall, Edmund Calamy, myself, Matthew Newcomen, and William Spurstow. Put our initials together in that order, rendering the double-*u* literally, and you have the name 'Smectymnuus,' by which we have signed ourselves."

John picked up the manuscript and unrolled it, rolled it backward to take out the curl, and flattened it upon the table. "May I read it?"

"Please. I have brought it for that."

After reading five pages Milton looked up. "This is not to be done speedily," he said. "Can you leave it with me?"

"Overnight, yes. But let me tell you what my purpose is. We would like your views on it and would be pleased to have you put your pen to it in any points you think might be made more forcefully."

The younger man was startled. "What are you thinking of,

Dr. Young! I have nothing to add to so impressive an author as 'Smectymnuus.' "

"Wrong, John, you have, though I appreciate your honest modesty. We wished to submit it to an outside eye before its publication. You have three things that led us to choose you. You are young, and there must be youth in this struggle; you are not of the clergy, and this fight will finally rest with laymen; lastly, you are a poet and our prose can bear the aid of your singing pen."

"Well," John said, "leave it with me. I shall study it and we will talk tomorrow."

Through the night hours John studied the reply to Bishop Hall. There was little that he could add to the skillful criticism of the five learned divines. But he felt himself caught up in a sense of struggle and conflict. His wrath against a Church of God ruled by worldly, political bishops rose hotly. He added to the pamphlet a bitter postscript, reaching out beyond the immediate answer to Bishop Hall to attack the whole institution of the bishopric. When Dr. Young and his collaborators read it they welcomed it gladly. It was made a part of the reply.

When the pamphlet of Smectymnuus appeared, a new drive and restlessness entered Milton. More than he knew, he had committed himself. It pained him to look squarely along the path he was treading, for it wound away from the high road of poetry. He remembered Galileo and Grotius. There was a duty for him as Christian and citizen. The craft of verse must wait. There was no choice.

Every man with a voice was raising it these days. His former landlord, Russell the tailor, would harangue for hours on the street corner. Sidewalk orators, balladmongers, clergymen, and scholars argued with equal passion.The quarrel was truly of the people. Samuel Butler, in doggerel verses, told the story.

> The Oyster women locked their fish up
> And trudged away to cry "No Bishop!"
>
> . . . .
>
> Botchers left old clothes in the lurch,
> And fell to turn and patch the Church.

John could not address himself to Russell the tailor, dash off handbills, or laugh down matters with jingles. It was not his way. But Thomas Young had shown him a road and he hastened down it.

He gave himself over furiously to preparing a solo argument of his own. Everything but the teaching of his pupils was thrust aside for the work. In May, 1641, Thomas Underhill published the first controversial pamphlet by John Milton, entitled *Of Reformation Touching Church-Discipline in England*. It was unsigned and took the form of a supposed address to a friend.

The controversial pamphlets of that day were noted for streams of abuse heaped upon opponents by the writers. It was a style; weak, perhaps, but expected. Milton at once showed a high talent for abuse, insult and rough language. His are no pussyfoot pamphlets. In this one his complaint was that the Episcopal system had set the Church of England apart from all of European Protestantism. A Protestant union was desired by everyone but prevented by King and High Church. None other than his friend Hugo Grotius had urged a plan for a Protestant union upon Archbishop Laud and been rebuffed.

Now that the poet had become pamphleteer he continued his new literary work with a vengeance. Pamphlets flew thick and fast, from Bishop Hall, his son, the Smectymnuusans, and Milton. It is impossible, today, to look upon the array of titles as they followed one another, without laughing. Seventeenth century scholarship was brilliant, sometimes profound, but definitely heavy handed. In its day this was a matter of course and nothing else was expected. Today the titles would strike us as pompous and academic. Strung together they roll up an astonishing effect. The reply to Smectymnuus had been, *A Defense of the Humble Remonstrance*. Milton flung back, *Animadversions upon the Remonstrant's Defense against Smectymnuus,* a masterpiece of slugging epithet. Previously he had published *Of Prelatical Episcopacy and whether it may be deduced from the Apostolical Times*. When the son of Bishop Hall entered the fray Milton's reply to his pamphlet was, *Apology against a Pamphlet called a Modest Confutation of the Animadversions*. Smectymnuus spoke up in "his" own behalf with *A Vindication of the Answer to a Humble Remonstrance,* leaving Bishop Hall, who had started the whole thing, to finish it with *A Short Answer to the Tedious Vindication of Smectymnuus*.

Meanwhile there had been one more pamphlet of Milton's, quite the best considered and most worthy of survival. This was *The Reason of Church Government Urged Against Prelacy*. It was the first pamphlet openly signed by him. Published by John Rothwell, it was put on sale at the *Sunne* in St. Paul's Churchyard in February, 1642.

This was the work in which John came of age as a writer of prose, the first which showed an eloquence in this form worthy of his verse. There is less abuse and violent language. He begins, in fact, with the principle "that persuasion certainly is a more winning, and more manlike way to keep men in obedience than fear."

But the scrupulous conscience and self-examining honesty of John Milton are clearly highlighted here. It is as though he had sat at his desk and said to himself, "I must make sure of myself, then make them sure of me." He explains at length his reasons for turning from his chosen task to enter this quarrel, and why he feels himself able to take part in it.

His first hope has always been, he admits, that "by labor and intent study (which I take to be my portion in this life) . . . I might perhaps leave something so written to aftertimes, as they should not willingly let it die." No one ever uttered a nobler purpose for writing. If in anything it is in poetry that he is sure of his ability to do this. Yet now he turns to prose, a "manner of writing wherein I have but the use of my left hand." It is the call of conscience that has steered him. "When God commands to take the trumpet and blow a dolorous or a jarring blast, it lies not in man's will what he shall say or what he shall conceal."

He shows us also, as he had assured his father when the old gentleman had questioned his choice of a career, that he is concerned for the seemliness of his position as a man born to comfort. You must not shirk your duty, he says to himself, when "ease and leisure was given thee for thy retired thoughts out of the sweat of other men." There must not come a time, after the bitter struggles of his church, when some might say, "where canst thou show any word or deed of thine which might have hastened her peace?"

All these explanations made, he strikes firmly for Presbyterianism as the form of church government clearly and exclusively authorized by the Scriptures. All else, whether of bishops or of popes, is contrary to the word of God.

"Presbyter" is the Greek word for "Elder"; a Presbyterian Church is one ruled by Elders.

John is now a young man of thirty-three, wrestling over theology with graybeards. But he makes no bones of it. His case is well reasoned and he is confident of it. "If any man incline to think I undertake a task too difficult for my years, I trust through the supreme enlightening assistance [of the Bible] far otherwise; for my years, be they few or many, what imports it, so they bring reason?"

But while John schooled himself in the art of harsh words, England was seeing harsh deeds. The political side of this death struggle was in eruption. In 1641, after the hard-handed Earl of Strafford was its prisoner, the Parliament had charged him with high treason. His crimes were great and bloody: arrest without warrant, punishment after false trials, the terrorism of spies and secret judgments, warmongering. Yet they were crimes of such scope and nature as to fall outside the legalistic limits of any single law by which he might be easily nailed. Parliament took a quick course and doomed him with a Bill of Attainder, a special act of Parliament, flatly accusing him and condemning him at one and the same time, outside the processes of the civil law. This was punishing tyranny of the one by tyranny of the many.

Such a procedure is expressly forbidden by the Constitution of the United States. But Parliament was standing on no technicalities such as had enabled Strafford to grind his heel upon Englishmen. He was beheaded on the fourteenth of May. When the ax fell there were some groans from the assembled crowd, but an observer reported, "Many that came to town to see the execution rode in triumph back, waving their hats, and with all expressions of joy through every town they went, crying, 'His head is off! His head is off!'"

Archbishop Laud was arrested and imprisoned also, in 1640. Puritan hatred was as great against him as against Strafford. A common cry was heard in the streets, punning upon his name: "Give great praise to God, but give little Laud to the devil!"

The Puritan pamphleteers partly had their way. The services of the Church of England were simplified and bishops were removed from their accustomed places in the House of Peers. A plot against Parliament was rumored and set London buzzing with visions of a second Guy Fawkes Gunpowder Plot.

During the hot debates that were daily waged in the Commons there clustered around Whitehall jostling mobs of citizenry. Milton was often among them, seeking to follow the debates on the fate of the Episcopal system. He was crushed and shoved in the milling swarm of courtiers and poorly clad workmen and apprentices.

Historic nicknames were in birth here in the crowds at Whitehall. The courtiers and noblemen were derided by the apprentices as mere adventurers and soldiers of fortune, by the name of "cavaliers." In turn, the cropped haircuts of the apprentices caused the courtiers to dub them "roundheads." Both terms stuck. Henceforth, in the long struggle between King and Parliament the followers of the one were generally called cavaliers; the followers of the other, roundheads, regardless of their actual station in life.

Charles, meantime, strode along in his path of headstrong follies. He demanded of Parliament the surrender, on false charges of treason, of its great leader, Pym, and four of his chief supporters. The Commons refused to surrender them and sent them into hiding.

On the fourth of January, 1642, there was a showdown. Milton and Alexander Gill went early to Whitehall to watch the outcome of the crisis. Charles himself, trailed by a group of cavaliers, entered the House of Commons and arrogantly took the floor, addressing himself to the chairman, "Mr. Speaker, I must for a time borrow your chair!"

A tense silence enveloped the House. The King surveyed the chamber insolently, well aware that the men he sought were long since in hiding. This was a disciplinary demonstration that he had determined to make. He addressed the members.

"Gentlemen, I am sorry for this occasion of coming unto you. Yesterday I sent a sergeant-at-arms upon a very important occasion to apprehend some that by my command were accused of high treason, whereunto I did expect obedience and not a message. Treason has no privilege, Parliamentary or otherwise, and, therefore, I am come to know if any of these persons that were accused are here."

No voice was raised in reply.

"I must have them wheresoever I find them."

Still the chamber was silent, tense, expectant. Charles struck at the Speaker's stand impatiently with his riding crop. "Is Mr. Pym here?" Turning to Lenthall, the Speaker, he demanded, "Are any of the five traitors here?"

Lenthall, trembling, threw himself upon his knees, saying, "I can reply, Your Majesty, only what the House instructs me."

"Well, well," Charles snapped in irritation, "no matter. I think my eyes are as good as another's." He turned back and swept the seated members with his gaze. "I see my birds are flown," he said finally, "but I do expect you will send them to me."

The King made his way from Parliament. At once the house broke out into a fury of resentment. Milton and Gill thoughtfully made their way through the excited mob to the quieter neighborhood of Aldersgate. Both were grim-faced. There was clearly no dealing with this manner of king.

Charles's outrage brought matters to a head. Parliament defied him and withheld its men. Six days later the King abandoned London to muster forces while his queen sailed for the Continent with all the jewels of the crown to shop for munitions. The cavalier followers of the King flocked to him. No reconciliation was possible. The Parliament worked feverishly to raise an army to uphold the defiant course it was steering now. Civil war was upon England.

One of the bold Puritan spirits of the House of Commons was a country gentleman named Oliver Cromwell, who had played little part in the debates of Parliament. Like Milton, he was a graduate of Cambridge. Moving swiftly, now, he swept upon the university with a small band of followers and seized its treasures of silver plate, before Charles had time to add them to his scanty war chest.

Charles raised his banners in August at Nottingham. In October the first large encounter, at Edgehill, had dubious results, leaning in advantage toward the King. Charles's forces, under his dashing nephew Rupert, advanced almost to London. The city was in panic. Nearly everyone withdrew within the old walls. Fortifications were thrown up and trenches dug in the streets.

Milton, although his house in Aldersgate was outside the walls of the old city and in the very path of the advance, sat tight. Refusing to take refuge, he continued to teach his flock in his accustomed routine. With tongue in cheek he wrote the sonnet, *When the Assault Was Intended to the City,* serving notice to any conquering officer who might sweep through, that here dwelt one of that breed without whose services no deed of valor could live for future ages.

> Captain or colonel, or knight in arms,
> Whose chance on these defenceless doors may seize,
> If deed of honour did thee ever please,
> Guard them, and him within protect from harms.
> He can requite thee, for he knows the charms
> That call fame on such gentle acts as these,
> And he can spread thy name o'er lands and seas,
> Whatever clime the sun's bright circle warms.
> Lift not thy spear against the Muses' bower:
> The great Emathian conqueror bid spare
> The house of Pindarus, when temple and tower
> Went to the ground: and the repeated air
> Of sad Electra's poet had the power
> To save the Athenian walls from ruin bare.

The danger to the city lifted. Charles removed, for a time, to quarters at Oxford. The fight was begun past recall. The champions of plain religion, the rawboned Puritans, now must rally to their banners, in the scriptural charge to "war a good warfare." Charles and his cavaliers might mock at them as eccentrics, but they would find them formidable warriors.

Chapter 6

The Fair Maid of Oxford

MAY WAS a month that always made John restless. It is the dire enemy of Puritans and scholars for it plays ducks and drakes with the soberest of them if nature takes its course and is not too ringed about with hedges of discipline and sober zeal. Milton was always open to its lures and its warm fragrance swept his lighter nature to the front, driving his austere spirit into the somber caves of his deeper thoughts. It was the time of "L'Allegro."

In this May of 1643 there was a lull in the civil war. John had written himself dry in his series of formidable pamphlets. He awoke upon its first morning with a sudden flood of revolt against the daily grubbing of Latin with Puritanical little boys, the sober intellectual prodigies of his own creation. He pondered his rebellious mood as he dressed and made a swift decision. " 'If 'twere done,' " he muttered to himself, " 'twere well it were done quickly.' "

"Father," he announced at the breakfast table, "I must have a vacation."

The old gentleman peered at his son in astonishment. "Vacation?" For the last two years such a frenzy of scholarship and concentration had reigned in the household as to make it intolerable. The elder Milton had crept about the house from room to room, careful not to disturb the thoughts and studies of the master, until he himself had been driven to a long vacation from the strain of merely looking on, and had spent some months with Christopher and his wife at Reading.

The round and solemn eyes of the Phillips boys were fixed owlishly upon their uncle in a like amazement. The great effect of his announcement suddenly embarrassed him.

"Well," he added, half apologetically, "and there is an errand I should do."

"What is that, John?"

"It is now nearly fourteen years since, at Cambridge, I lent your acquaintance, Mr. Richard Powell, five hundred pounds. He has paid me a dribble of interest now and again. I would be glad to collect the sum in such troublous times. I thought I would call upon him for it."

Mr. Milton shook his head. "I had forgotten the matter these many years," he said. "You are a bad businessman, John, to let it run so. Like as not you will not get it. I think it is as well you became a poet and no scrivener."

"Ah, but I have some forethought," John said, cheerfully. "For Squire Powell lives at Forest Hill, near Oxford. While Charles is quartered there he may be prospering from the great gathering of troops and followers. I hope to catch him with a full purse."

"Hmmm," the old man muttered doubtfully, "I mistrust the presence of Charles to bring prosperity to anyone."

"Well, we shall see. It eases my conscience to leave the boys in your charge since I make the pretext of an errand. There will be some further point to a sojourn near Oxford. I shall gather news, perhaps, on the intentions of the King."

He turned to his nephews who had finished breakfast and sat upon the edges of their chairs awaiting orders. "Well, young masters, what say you to a vacation?"

The brothers eyed their master with mistrust. Edward Phillips spoke up cautiously. "We shall regret our studies, Uncle."

"Come!" said Milton, gathering his brows into a scowl, "let me have no hypocrisy! Take your brief holiday while I am gone, and if you are hungry for drudgery you may read your Latin grammar by yourselves and invent a geometry of your own like Master Pascal, the Frenchman."

"Yes, Uncle!" both boys shouted, with the sudden dawning that the thing was real. Together they dashed off into the garden.

His whole being expanding with a rich glow of good feeling and high spirits, John Milton cast behind him the last thoughts of sober duty, exchanged a look with his father, and laughed.

Oxford was in a spirit of carnival. Charles's court was, for the time, established there. All the gay blades and cavalier spirits of the land were drawn together in his following. The pleasure spirit of relaxed soldiery prevailed. There were beautiful maidens aplenty, both in the blooded families of royal followers and in the rustic country girls whose quiet life was invaded with this massive pageantry.

John looked upon the show with disapproval; not the narrow censorship of the Puritan who preached against enjoyment of life, for he was there in the very spirit of spring himself. His scorn was for this scene of revelry and courtliness when, as he saw it, its occasion was the mustering of forces by which a treacherous king sought to grind away the liberties of his people.

He did not stand out among the throng as a Puritan. His clothing was of quality, though simple in style. The fine, clear cameo of his features, framed by a handsome richness of hair for which any preening courtier might envy him, gave him still the appearance of his twenties rather than the thirty-five years which he had passed. The girls of Oxford eyed him with approval on the streets and wondered what young lordling he might be.

This was no place for him. He left the town of Oxford and

went to the nearby rural village of Forest Hill. There he found an inn and took his lodgings.

This countryside of woods and pastures and gentle hills was beautiful in its Maytime cloak. John wandered down the green lanes in the general direction of the Powell home. It was long years since he had been here and he remembered it none too well. Still, this country had a meaning for him. It was the earlier seat of the Milton family. In this vicinity had lived his Papist grandfather, Richard Milton, with whom the elder John had fallen out.

As he strolled in the shade of the tall yew hedges of Holford's Close, a little cavalcade swept down upon him and jarred him out of his reverie. A young girl, riding a spirited dappled pony, had dashed around a corner of the hedgerow full upon him, followed by two running boys. A collision, head on, seemed certain and he braced himself to bear the shock. With a little scream, half of laughter, the young rider swerved her small steed. John was barely grazed, but the sudden shift unseated the girl and pitched her squarely into his arms.

Milton staggered from the impact but kept his footing, holding the now laughing girl tightly, in bewilderment. Gaining his wits he set her down and straightened his hat which had been knocked askew. Another moment brought him more fully to his senses and he reached again for his hat, this time to sweep it off and bow to the unembarrassed girl before him.

Dignity was no part of the scene. John stood bowing, rumpled and bewildered. The unrepentant pony, turning when it lost its rider, was now impudently nuzzling the pockets of the stranger in hope of sweets.

The girl before him was a fountain of laughter. "Sir," she said, "thank you for your quickness, and please, please forgive me."

John was almost wordless. "Why, it is nothing," he said, hastily, "you might as well forgive me for blocking your way."

She had hardly heard his reply and was now talking to the pony. "Clover!" she cried, "come away from the gentleman! Must you nearly knock him down and then rob his pockets! Robin, catch him!"

The smaller of the two boys seized the reins of the little creature and drew him aside. John's eyes were fixed still upon the girl before him.

"Will you tell me your name?"

"My name is Mary Powell." She indicated the younger boy, who held the bridle of the pony, "This is my brother Robin, and," gesturing to the taller boy, "this is my brother Dick. Dick is older than I and much more grave."

Both boys bowed. All looked expectantly at John.

"Surely you are not the daughter of Richard Powell?" he asked.

"Oh, but I am," she cried, in surprise. "Do you know my father?"

"I have a little business with him. I am John Milton, of London."

"Then you must come along with us. We will take you to our house. It is the least courtesy to a guest, after half killing him on his way. Come!"

So he found himself escorted to the house by the children of the man from whom he had come to claim a debt.

Richard Powell was a justice of the peace. He was a fervent royalist and a country squire, living on rich lands of a confiscated abbey. He had sprung from one of those families which had prospered when Henry VIII had broken with Rome and seized the holdings of the Church several generations before, dividing much of its lands among his favorites and their friends.

The King's quarters at Oxford might have meant some prosperity to Powell. The produce of his fields and poultry yards, his wagons and carts, the cheeses from the cheese house operated by his busy wife, were all sources of money. But those responsibilities that fell directly to him were no more than halfheartedly carried out. Such profits as he reaped went speedily in entertainment and extravagance. He preferred to make an excuse of the occasional enforced "contributions" that were exacted from his chicken yards, to justify his failure to flourish. He was a loyal King's man, he protested, and had no wish to profit by His Majesty's misfortunes.

The stout, talkative squire, with his short-trimmed beard, took a bland and lordly manner with his creditor. Of course it had been a long time. It was largely oversight. The present was an unfortunate moment. Yes, he could understand that it might seem as though cash were flowing a bit more freely through his hands, but actually this was not the case. The King's forces made many demands which a loyal subject, he stressed the phrase reproachfully, could not refuse. There was no profit in anything these days, and all was so unsettled. He would see about keeping up the interest, but surely the principal could be permitted to wait a little longer.

Milton was firm. Mr. Powell must realize that the unsettled times were all the more reason for this long-standing matter to be closed. It would be best to have it over with now. Then everyone would be able to forget about it.

There is no reason, the squire said to himself, why I should upset my applecart to pay a sum to this traitor to His Majesty. If he wants to be a Parliament man, why then he deserves no better and my own conscience is free.

Milton was unyielding; the Cambridge youth had known how to be so, the man knew no less.

Why, then, the squire must have time to think it over. He would have to cast about and see where he might be able to raise the money. There were some of his relatives he could approach though all of them were really as hard hit as he himself had been. In spite of being on different sides of the fence they could both agree that times were bad. Suppose Mr. Milton had to raise five hundred pounds in a hurry. He would then understand. Well, perhaps he did have to. True, it had no real bearing on the case. Well, then, in conclusion, Mr. Milton had better return home and he would write to him as soon as he had looked into the possibilities of getting cash.

John observed that he had some time at his disposal and would be in the neighborhood for at least a few weeks. That should give the squire ample time. And so the interview was ended on a seemingly cordial note.

If he had insisted only mildly and shown no hurry to conclude affairs and be off from Forest Hill, it was because, as he talked, the merry face and dark hair of the daughter were clearer in his vision than the bearded chin of the squire before him. The mind that was so strong had seized strongly on this image and would not yield it up to other thoughts.

In the ensuing days John Milton and Mary Powell saw much of one another. John had visited a friend, who lived nearby, the young clergyman, Roger Agnew, and found him married to Mary's cousin. At the Agnews' they found a common meeting ground, which soon carried over to include the lanes and meadows around the Powell home.

To John the young girl, seventeen, was a breath of that very spring which always wrought such power over him. The innocence and charm of her blithe nature banished, for a time, even his well-beloved "divine philosophy." As for Mary, this handsome man, grave but gracious, gentle and courteous with stately ways, quite enthralled her. She knew he held to the Parliament's side; she knew her father owed a sum of money to him which he was ill-disposed to pay. But his noble bearing and rich flow of words had charmed her. From her older and wiser cousin, Rose Agnew, she heard such words of praise of Milton, and such reports of fame, she felt herself quite swept away.

The sound of his voice, as they walked together through the hedgerows, was like music. There was a majestic flow of language that carried her as upon wings, when often she did not understand what he said. He sometimes talked as though she were not there, and it was at times like these that she listened with the greatest pleasure and least understanding. There was that in him so different from the other men she knew. He seemed, though she knew not why, of a higher and superior order. It was thrilling to be wooed by him, for wooing it was fast becoming.

John spoke of music and verse to her and quoted poetry. Words of the great poet Spenser, to whom he had often looked for inspiration, came to his lips:

> Men call you fair, and you do credit it,
> For that yourself ye daily such do see:
> But the true fair, that is the gentle wit,
> And virtuous mind, is much more praised of me.

John, John, an inner voice sometimes chided him, she is the very opposite of what you say. A lovely girl, and fresh, and charming, and lithesome as the spring. But she's a toy, a plaything, that knows not what you are or what you would become. She cannot match you in anything but laughter, and there she can so outdo you it were a shame to challenge her. Yes, but she was lovely and she haunted his dreams. That same "tireless love with spangled wings" that had wearied his heart in Cambridge stood evermore beside him.

Still, he reasoned, she has a virtuous mind if not a gentle wit. She could be taught, would learn so easily.

Mind you, said the voice, you cannot tutor a wife, as you would tutor John and Edward Phillips. You cannot take a cane to her, as you do to them, when they fail in their studies. And you would wish to do so, for anything less than full understanding of your deepest thoughts would surely vex you.

He brought her a book, one day, and urged her to read it. But she put it aside and turned to him, exclaiming, "I much prefer to talk than read. Tell me what is in it."

This troubled him. Still, he thought, that is not bad. She wishes me to instruct her. He felt a certain pleasure in the flattery and began to speak of books and scholars. But he felt her attention wandering, caught her eye and saw it blank. This angered him, and yet, she drew him back.

In the name of decent courtesy Richard Powell bade Milton dine with them. The Agnews were present, to help the talk along, for it skirted perilously around the wide gaps in faith and politics.

"May I speak to you aside, sir?" Milton asked of the squire when they had left the table.

Powell jumped as though a snake had bitten him and set his brain furiously to the preparation of excuses.

"It is not of money," John added.

Relieved but mystified, Powell led his guest into his small office.

"Now then, sir, in what way can I serve you?" he demanded, safely assured that it would not be with cash.

"I beg leave, sir, to be received at your house."

"But you are received, man. Why, you're here, that is."

"I mean as one who would seek to win your daughter's favor."

The squire stared at Milton almost with alarm, startled beyond belief. "Well, well sir, Mr. Milton. Mr. Milton, indeed!"

"You know my family, Mr. Powell. My father is an honorable and respected man. My own circumstances are those of dignity and security, my education is of the best, and I feel that I shall not fail to bring something of honor to myself. I make bold, therefore, to put my hopes before you."

"Come, Mr. Milton, there is no question of that, no question of you. I mistrust your leanings toward the Parliament, but then, well, England is in such a state, I cannot judge you. But I am amazed, astonished, taken aback. How have you spent your time here?"

"Honorably, sir. Mistress Mary and I have formed an acquaintance. If I did not feel there was some hope that she would have me I would not approach you. If I may feel that I have your permission. . . ."

"Yes, yes, of course. You have my consent, of course. Speak to the girl . . . that is, go your own way. We will be glad to receive you, but, well, it is a surprise. I must tell her mother."

"Not tonight, please. Let us have no more of the matter, this evening, till I have gone. It would embarrass me."

"Very well, my boy, that is, er, Mr. Milton. You do me honor, sir, great honor."

When the guests were gone the squire was near to bursting with his news. His wife, Mary, and Dick were together in the hall. He came in from the farewells outside, beaming with the importance of news breaking.

"Now then," he cried, heartily, "guess what! Our Mistress Mary has a suitor!"

Mary flushed a deep red and tried to disappear into her chair. Mrs. Powell flushed also, but with a different emotion. "What do you mean?" she demanded, suspiciously.

"The worthy Mr. Milton has asked if he may call on us to seek our Mary's favor!"

"You refused permission, I am sure!" cried Mrs. Powell, rising.

At this, Mary came alive and sat up anxiously.

"Why no, madam, I did not refuse!" retorted the squire, in confusion at the fierce assault. "Why, indeed, should I refuse, madam? He is a worthy man, honorable, of position."

The mother swung accusingly upon the girl. "Mary, child, you will not marry that stiff-necked, roundheaded Puritan!"

"Mother," she faltered, "he . . . he hasn't asked me."

"Oh, he will, he will, be sure of that!" the squire cried cheerfully. "He hasn't been to all this trouble for nothing. It almost makes me wonder if he came here for the money in the first place."

Mistress Powell flashed a withering look of rebuke upon her husband and turned her fierce gaze back upon the girl, questioningly.

"Indeed, he is no roundhead, Mother, but has the loveliest hair of any man I ever saw. He is handsome, Mother, and a distinguished gentleman and poet. Rose and Roger will tell you. He is almost famous."

"And what, then, will you do with a famous husband?" the mother demanded, softening her tone a little into a sort of despair. "You will find him harsh, as all Puritans are, sweet face and long hair notwithstanding. You are a simple, country girl. You will not be able to keep pace with him. It is unjust of him to ask you."

"He must surely be able to judge of that, Mother," Mary said bravely. "I know I am not a wise, worldly woman. But he knows that, too, and if he will choose me, why should I refuse?"

"Now then, let us not debate it longer with the girl tonight," Powell interposed. "Your mother and I will talk more of it," he said to the girl, gently. "Do you not worry yourself on the matter."

"I do not think she should marry a Parliament man," Dick blurted.

"Oh, be quiet. You are horrid, Dick!" Mary cried, flying at him.

"Now then, now then, both of you to bed!" Powell insisted firmly. "No more of it; absolutely no more. Good night, both of you!"

"Well, Mr. Powell," the mother said, when they were alone, "you are strangely bent upon this match, it seems to me. I should like an explanation."

"Come, come," he said, in a conciliating tone, "you are too drastic in your view of it. In the first place, it must be admitted, it is a good match."

"Yes, except that he is a Puritan and a Parliament man while we are Royalists and High Church. That is no small chasm of separation."

"Of course, that is regrettable. You know my loyalties well enough. Still, I talk with many who doubt the King will win back much of his power. They think conciliation will be reached. There is little enough to fear in the connection, perhaps. And then there is another thing to be remembered."

"Well?"

"The money, my dear, five hundred pounds. He is determined to have it and, you well know, we have not got it."

"Are you selling your daughter for five hundred pounds?" Mistress Powell demanded hotly.

"Oh, no, no! Of course not! How can you even speak such a thing!" the squire cried in horror. "Oh, certainly not! Consider, we are agreed already that it is a good match in all but one thing. Moreover, the child herself has fallen in love with him, quite understandably as she has put it herself. So you must admit it is merely an honest, fortunate, pleasing thought that a son-in-law will not make an unpleasantness over five hundred pounds which could only come from God knows where and forever ruin us. He will demand it, otherwise, mark me, and quite justly so. I do not blame him."

"Richard Powell, you are a sly and Jesuitical reasoner. It will end in grief. I say it and say it again. It will end in grief!"

The squire saw in this a surrender and was content.

Was ever so swift a courtship pressed by a sober man? John had lost no time, with the strong impulse ever in his nature, to urge his suit, once the way was paved. Mary, quite as swept away as he, was all as willing.

The dark-haired, pert-face girl was a drunkenness with him that would not be abated. She soaked into his fibers and trembled in his veins. And he was silent, silent but for the soft talk of a wooer. The muse that had wrought *canzonettas* for the queenly charms of worldly Leonora Baroni would not speak for the fresh, country girl. His muse was disquieted, mistrustful, but John would not hear her voice. Rather, he turned her past gifts to his purpose and recited to the romantic girl the sweetest strains of his already written verse.

Perhaps a hopeful chord of association was awakened in him when she asked, one day, if he loved music.

"Indeed, I do," he answered eagerly, "so well I cannot bear to listen to any but the best. My father is a fine musician and trained me well in it. Tell me, sweet Mary, do you play and sing?"

But he had blighted her confidence in her simple talent. She was frightened, as so often, by the intensity of his responses. She stood in a certain fear of his passionate enthusiasms for truth and beauty and conviction, so unlike the indifferent beliefs and interests of the men she knew. Now, scared at the consequences of her question, she would not admit to the simple, natural talents that she had.

"Oh, hardly, hardly at all. You would not think so. I only wish I had such gifts."

Then, cruelly, she was hurt by the glint of disappointment in his eye, as if this one point was of a greater importance than she knew, as if it had been almost a last hope, unspoken.

"You . . . you could teach me," she suggested, timidly.

"Yes," he said, brightening, "perhaps I could. I am sure you have a talent. I am sure you have, sweet."

The young man knew well that Mistress Powell did not like him. He knew well that the squire was sure the marriage would mean relief from the pressing debt. This he did not begrudge. The girl truly loved him, of that he was certain. What of the five hundred pounds? It had been an excuse for a Maytime journey, and the sweet month had rewarded him with a treasure beyond all gold.

So, with a whirlwind swiftness, pressed against all shocked scandal at such haste, John urged the marriage. He pleaded his need to return to London and the general unrest as reasons for the unusual haste. He would not be put off. To Mary it was thrilling that her suitor should brook no waits. It was a girl's dream.

Twenty-four days after John had set out from Aldersgate Street, Mary Powell became young Mistress Milton. He had sent on word to his father of the astonishing news so that the old man might not die of shock upon his returning. The jovial festivities of wedding, more lavishly cavalier than Puritan, were patiently borne by the eager bridegroom. Then, brimming with joy and passion, he set out in triumph with his bride for Aldersgate.*

* The tradition of Milton's marriage in 1643 is according to the version of Edward Phillips in his life of his uncle. On the other hand, modern Milton scholars consider it possible that these events may have fallen one year earlier, in 1642.

Chapter 7

"Clinging Mischief"

T HE HOUSE in Aldersgate Street now had the mistress it needed. Mr. Milton, shocked by the sudden news that John was returning with a bride, gathered himself together as best he could.

"Boys," he announced to John and Edward, "your uncle will bring back a wife with him, we must make the house ready."

The old man set the servants scurrying feverishly about in a great flurry of industry and then undid half their labors. So, when pretty Mary Milton crossed the threshold of her new home, it was clean—after a fashion. The old gentleman had ordered hands off the study and tidied it himself. The books piled upon the chairs were dusted spick and span. Countless small articles he had not been able to find a place for were shoved under chairs or behind the door. The litter of music manuscripts upon the father's desk stumped him until he thought to set a screen before it so that Mary might not notice it until she was more at home. To a quick glance the house was neat.

"Welcome, daughter, welcome!" The old gentleman embraced Mary warmly. She was a pretty thing, to be sure. "Well, John, my boy, you have fooled us all and quite taken us by storm. Confess, now, you had an intention of this when you left us so mysteriously."

"Oh, I think he did not," Mary said, laughing, "for he has

taken me quite by storm, Mr. Milton. He is so impetuous he will not be denied."

The father looked troubled. He had searched hard for an explanation. The only possible one seemed to lie in a secret intention, perhaps long planned. Swiftness, in a matter of this sort, seemed not only ill-advised, but unlike his son.

John was presenting the Phillips boys. "Now, young masters," he said, with heavy heartiness, "greet your aunt. I know you will obey her with the same duty and regard you bear toward me."

The boys bowed primly. "Welcome, Aunt," Ned said. "We will try to deserve your love."

"Perhaps you will help us with our studies," his brother added, hopefully.

Milton flushed.

"Oh," said Mary, with cheerful honesty, "I am sure that you both could help me more than I could you. But you will surely have my love." With that she kissed them.

All the men were silent for a moment, puzzled and embarrassed.

The next day Milton devoted to showing his bride the sights of London. She gazed with wonder at the Tower, the Houses of Parliament, the great bridges, the theaters. She saw the house and street where her husband had been born, and the school at St. Paul's where he had begun his education. The vast cathedral filled her with awe but her husband made light of it, complaining it had been profaned by worldly and corrupt bishops. Secretly she thought it wrong to set so little store by this great monument to God's worship and it dismayed her that worthy bishops, whom she had been taught to respect, should be so decried.

The crowded, jostling streets of the city, thronged now with Puritan zealots, half overcame her. The foul odors of the gutters seemed unbearable to one reared with the fresh fragrance of fields and dairies. The cries of vendors and hawkers, the mountebanks with apes or bears, the cooks' shops in Westminster with smoking dishes of roast meats and bowls of salad set out upon long trestles quite bewildered her with sights, sounds, and smells.

A change had come over John. He seemed suddenly sobered, almost to glumness. It troubled Mary and made her nervous. Her father-in-law, kind as he was, studied her strangely. She felt his eyes upon her often and lacked the courage to meet his gaze. It was well that she did not hear a few words that passed between her husband and his father on the second day.

"John," the old man said, "I am at a loss to understand you. I hope all will be well, but it is hard to think that you have done wisely."

Milton flared up in irritation. "Am I not of an age to marry and know my mind?" he demanded.

"Ah, son, there is no set age to know one's mind. Perhaps you know it very well. Then do you know your blood? She is a good and virtuous girl, and willing. But does she know to whom and what she has been wedded? I only hope you will not be unfair to her. Two opinions do not sit well on one bolster."

"Let us talk no more about it," John said, abruptly.

Now it appeared that the holiday was over. John pitched himself back into the routine of his duties with a special fever of concentration. The outside pupils resumed their morning attendance and the little school was in swing once more.

Mary found herself suddenly alone and idle. In the morning her husband was shut up with his pupils. In the afternoons, and sometimes in the evenings, he labored at his desk with the mysterious and endless writings which always absorbed him. This, she supposed, was how poets and writers did their work but it made for dismal households.

She tried to occupy herself but there was little enough to do. A maid was engaged to carry out the work of the household and prepare the meals. Mary supervised and busied herself with simple tasks done twice over. Still time hung heavily. The need for quiet in the house so much of the time oppressed her. She began to sit in the garden and her mind strayed back toward Forest Hill and the cheerful, bustling household to which she was accustomed. She had not dreamed of such a thing as this hushed schoolmaster's barrack.

She tried to make real the false orderliness that had greeted her arrival. Milton was gently tolerant and merely cautioned her not to disturb his books and papers. But these seemed everywhere. She tried to straighten out the old man's desk but the next morning he complained that he could not find a new song Harry Lawes had sent to him.

"You must have put it in the kitchen fire," he said, fretfully, at breakfast. "I had no more than scanned it and now it's gone. I wanted to go through that batch of papers that you burned. I knew there were wrong things in it."

"But indeed, Father-in-law," Mary cried, "there was truly nothing that I burned save scraps of paper you had yourself already torn across and left scattered. I only gathered them up."

"Well, it's missing," he insisted. "You must have got it mixed in. Besides, there might have been notes and reminders on those scraps. A man has to use what comes to hand. Don't touch my desk. John, you don't have her among your papers, I notice. No more should I."

Mary was in tears and left the table. John hastened after her. "Now, sweet," he said, truly concerned for her, "it is nothing. If anything is missing it is an accident, I know. Do not trouble with our desks. There is no need for you to do so and you will never teach us to keep them in order, I fear."

The old gentleman found the missing song under his pillow and came to Mary to apologize. But the tears were shed and already dried.

Milton's friends came to greet his wife. In the first week, any afternoon or evening was apt to find its caller. Young Andrew Marvell, just out of Cambridge, a light-spirited poet, was the first to come. Like John before him, he was bound for the Continent and wanted letters to the men of Florence and Rome. He twitted Mary and praised her beauty so that she quite enjoyed his visit.

Others were not so cheerful. Mrs. Catharine Thompson, the Reverend Thomas Young, Dr. Davis and his learned daughter Mildred, came at different times. Mary was crushed under the weight of scholarly conversation and shocked at the talk against the King and bishops. Her husband's friends spoke innocently to her in languages she did not understand about subjects she had never even heard of. When she excused herself and pleaded her ignorance there were surprised silences. Milton was quick to leap into the breach and cover, where he could, her lack of knowledge. Nothing was meant in malice, yet she saw the flush of mortification that came sometimes to his cheeks and the check she put upon the conversations. She sometimes wept after these ordeals.

Christopher Milton, the lawyer, came to town and dined at Aldersgate Street. She found him as different from her husband as the sea from the land. But if this brother-in-law, in his views on King and church, might be closer to her it was no comfort. There was a cold, half-insolent curiosity in him, and a sly, malicious bent of wit which he turned against her subtly until John, in anger, bade him be silent or take himself away.

John was a harsh schoolmaster, the more so as he did not

love the task. He flogged his pupils when they did not master their lessons well. He had forgotten, perhaps, his troubles with the Reverend William Chappell at Cambridge. Moreover, these boys were younger and it was not a question, as it had been with him, of their desire to learn more but rather the failure to do so. He believed in firm discipline and physical punishment. A bit of caning was tonic for their souls.

The first cries she heard from the schoolroom brought Mary hastening to the door, fearful that some accident had occurred. She was shocked to see her husband sternly caning John Phillips.

"Oh!" she cried out, "the poor boy! What has happened?"

Milton released the crying boy and came out of the classroom, closing the door behind him, all but cutting off the sound of the sobbing.

"Now, my sweet," he said, sharply, "you must not interfere between the boys and me again. I am merely doing my task."

"But must you beat him so?" she asked.

"You are a gentle girl, my dear," her husband said, more tolerantly, "and perhaps it may seem harsh to you. It is a discipline, however, approved by God, Himself, and practiced by all wise men. The spirit of youth must learn to bend itself to the demands of scholarship. This cannot be done without some pain, no more can any other worthy thing in our lives."

"But I have not seen my brothers taught in this way."

"The reason for that, my little clinging mischief, lies in no fault of mind but in your brothers' education. They are not great scholars, you will admit."

"But they were happy children."

"That's as it may be. We must have, also, happy, worthy men. Such I am seeking to build. Do not interfere again, I pray, for it will destroy all discipline."

So the cheerless sound of crying boys became a morning

noise to which the young girl found she must accustom herself. For all she could do, her spirits sank lower. John was not unkind to her. Indeed, he seemed to be in the grip of some secret suffering of his own of which she felt an impulsive wish to help relieve him. But he did not speak of it. She felt the effort which he made to be gentle and tender with her. He had stuck to the phrase his tongue had chanced upon and called her often his "clinging mischief." It expressed, more than he fully knew, the rueful affection that he felt for her.

She tried to read. One morning she searched over the books on the packed shelves. They overcame her with their ponderousness. So many of them were in Latin, Italian, or other tongues. Others were of such a heaviness that it made her head ache to think of them. A volume of Shakespeare seemed the friendliest thing about. She took it with her to the garden and opened it. At the beginning was a sonnet which she knew to be her husband's and she felt proud, although she little understood it.

The pages of Shakespeare were not unknown to her. Desperate loneliness and the keen wish to draw nearer to her husband's interests kept her at the pages and she read with pleasure. But the perverse way of chance led her to a thousand themes that pricked her sorrow. Portia shamed her, seeming like the wise women of her husband's acquaintance. "A light wife doth make a heavy husband," the page said. She did not know the real meaning of the words, that a woman of bad morals brought grief to a husband, but took it in terms of Milton's learning and her ignorance. Indeed her husband was heavy. Was it then some fault of hers, a hopeless lightness, that afflicted him?

In this house, even the small boys were heavy, so pompous and unlike her own gay brother Robin. She thought, with shame, that she might more fittingly be romping with them,

were they but natural themselves, than sitting as helpmeet
to their stern master. If only there had been in this house that
was all *Il Penseroso* some moments of *L'Allegro's* once warmly
invoked but now forgotten "Jest, and youthful Jollity. . . . And
Laughter holding both his sides."

Impatiently she flipped the pages of the big book and
sought a less thorny text. *The Taming of the Shrew* was a gay,
laughing thing. She had seen it once at Oxford with glee and
merriment. Why might not her husband have a little of the
Italian gaiety of this Petruchio? He spoke often enough of
Italy. She looked again at the page. This time the chastened
Katharine addressed her:

> Such duty as the subject owes the prince,
> Even such a woman oweth to her husband.

Surely she was not scant of her duty. Yet somehow it seemed
not enough. The spark of resentment had crept into her breast,
unrealized. "Such duty as the subject owes the prince?" Indeed,
this was a strange comparison that she should chance upon. Was
ever subject more undutiful to prince than this, her husband,
with his bold scorn of King and challenge to the church? Was
this an example with which to teach a wife her duty?

A month had barely passed for the new Mistress Milton, the
weeks seeming to extend themselves into a dismal, endless
plain. Milton had gone, in the afternoon, upon an errand in the
city, taking his father with him. The boys were at their everlasting books. Unannounced, came Richard Powell, her older
brother, with her cousin, Ralph Hewlett.

"Dick! Ralph!" Mary cried, flinging herself into their arms
almost hysterically.

"Well, little sister," Dick said, "we came to see how you are
faring with the roundheads."

"Hush!" she said. The Phillips boys had come, curiously, to

investigate the tumult. Mary introduced them. "Now, then," she added, with a little malice, "we will not disturb your studies, Ned and John, but we will go into the garden and leave you to your tasks."

"Mary," Dick said, when they had left the house, "I am shocked to see you as you look! How does this villain treat you?"

Mary burst into tears. "I am so unhappy," she sobbed, "I long so much for home."

The young men were appalled. "Has he mistreated you?" Ralph Hewlett demanded.

"Oh, no, no, no! He is very kind. He tries to be, anyway," she said, attempting to check her sobs. "It is just . . . this place . . . is so unlike our life . . . so dry . . . so deathly. It's my fault. I am not bright enough to be his wife. He will become ashamed of me. I am so ignorant."

Her brother was hotly indignant. "Now then!" he cried out, "I will not see my sister like this. He married you of his own choice. You are no ignorant girl but a girl of a good family and knowing all that befits a plain, good woman. I shall take you back with me this very day!"

"Oh, no! I could not leave him now, for a visit. It is so soon. He would not understand."

"Nevertheless, you must come back with us. Why you will fade off to a vapor if I leave you here. A few weeks of fresh, clean air at Forest Hill will strengthen you to come back to this dungeon if you must."

"I could not leave now."

"Come, we will find an excuse. I meant to tell you, Father is not well."

"Is he really ill?" she asked, alarmed.

"Well, yes. It is his old trouble of the stomach. I guess it is no worse than another time, but still, he is a sick man. It will serve for our need."

Mary flushed. "It would be wicked to lie to Mr. Milton."

"It is no lie. Your father is sick. Only a monster would keep you from his side. Come, I will arrange it."

She could not check him for she did not wish to. With all her heart she longed for the fields and hedges of Forest Hill and the merriment of her father's house.

When John came home, in the late afternoon, he was disturbed to find his visitors. He greeted his wife's kinsmen with real cordiality, but the sudden visit seemed to him to augur something ill. This fitted well with Dick's intent and he lost no time.

"We have come to ask that my sister return home with us for a few days, sir. Our father is ill."

"Indeed!" cried Milton, "I am sorry of it. Is he gravely sick?"

"Well, we cannot surely tell. It is a chronic trouble, of the stomach, that makes us fear for him, for it grows worse yearly. He longs to see her."

No thought of suspicion entered Milton's mind. Wholly honest men are not quick to suspect dishonesty in others. Yet he felt, somehow, a bewilderment he could not understand.

"What do you wish to do?" he asked, turning to his wife.

She flushed and lowered her eyes. "I do not wish to leave you," she faltered, "but I should like to go to my father. Could you not come with me?"

Dick was appalled. This had not been planned. But the lack of skill or practice in deceit had confused Mary into a wise stratagem. Milton was touched.

"No, little clinging mischief, that is impossible," he said, gravely. "I cannot leave my duties so soon again. But you must surely go, without delay, so that you may hasten back to me. It is cruel to lose a sweet wife in so short a time, though I fear," he said, in troubled uncertainty, "that I do not make you so happy as I should wish. When you have come back we will mend this."

Leaving that evening was a thing Milton would not hear of. But in the morning the three departed. John kissed his wife fondly, gave her a generous purse, bade her remember him to her father and to hasten back to him as soon as she might. He stood thoughtfully in the doorway, as they left. Somehow, though why he could not tell, he felt a little hurt. After a time he turned away and went in to his pupils.

Two days after Mary had left, the little family group sat at their midday meal. Since she had gone John had kept her place laid at the table. Was she not still a member of the family, though absent?

"We should soon hear from Mary," he said to his father. "I hope it does not go badly with Mr. Powell."

"Powell is younger than I am," the old man said with satisfaction, "but he's lived harder and indulged his belly in every appetite. It will take him off before me. You shall see."

"I do not think Mr. Powell is very ill, Uncle," Ned Phillips said gravely.

"Why not, Ned?"

"That's what Mistress Milton's brother said."

"What do you mean?" Milton demanded sharply.

The boy flushed a trifle at the stir he was causing. "We heard him, Uncle. He said it was not worse than any other time but it would serve their need. Then our aunt said it would be wicked to lie to Mr. Milton. So her brother said it was no lie, her father was sick, and only a monster would keep her from his side."

"How did you hear this?"

"They were in the garden. We were near the window."

Milton rose, pale and breathless. "It was wrong of you to eavesdrop," he said, shortly, and left the table.

That afternoon he wrote to Roger Agnew, at Forest Hill, with a single question. There was a terrible fear in his heart that he dared not examine. He fought it down with fierce concentration upon studies and duties. The house became silent. Even his father said nothing to him.

In three days his answer came from Agnew. No word, meanwhile, had come from Mary. He felt his worst fears were confirmed and hesitated long before suddenly ripping open the letter. So far as he knew, Agnew wrote, Mr. Powell was well. He had only just seen the family and knew they were all delighted at Mary's visit.

Pain and rage mingled and strove together in him. At once he wrote a harshly worded letter to Mary. "I am amazed that you can take pleasure in a leave so ill-obtained. It is a pain, grief, and outrage to me that you should have so conducted yourself. I am moved to suppose that it was chiefly due to the wrong influence of the two young men, your brother and cousin, from whom no more, I am now led to think, could have been expected. Impulsive acts of bad judgment we may all be guilty of. Such I construe this to be and shall charitably count it such. I shall expect, however, your immediate return."

A week passed before an answer came from Forest Hill. It was not addressed in Mary's hand and when opened proved to come from the squire himself.

Sir [it said], The unseemly, harsh and cantankerous letter lately received by my daughter is such as I might expect from a round-headed traitor to England and His Majesty. We have repented of the connection which, through a folly we cannot understand but lay up to your subtle importuning, we so hastily and ill-advisedly permitted. My daughter has had enough of the grave, unnatural life you led her to and will remain, henceforth, in the bosom of her loving and repentant family. You need not look to have her back again.

Your obedient servant . . .

John had been choking down a festering suspicion that now burst out in ugly reality. He sat rigid for some time, the letter crumpled in stiff fingers. An intolerable, burning shame of humiliation wound about and enveloped him like a shroud. He felt a hot flush and an aching, boardlike stiffness of his cheeks. He looked at the naked truth he had cloaked and shaded since returning with his bride, the truth which had thrust him into morose fits of brooding almost before his wife had explored the home to which he had brought her.

All the ripe anticipations were disappointed. He felt debased. He refused to suppose a failure in himself toward Mary. The answer must lie in the great gulf of mind and spirit which he now admitted lay between them.

John ate no dinner that night and penned himself away, shunning the sight of his father and the boys. He lay awake upon his bed in the hot summer night and thrashed about in his torment of spirit. The great branching oak of his pride, that had put forth rich leaves and mighty branches with his growing fame, was cleft at the root and felled in splintered wreckage. He could not keep a wife. That was what the gossips would say. In the face of the mocking, hostile world, this woman had left him, a month after marriage, and brazenly refused to come back to her lord and liege.

There was a wild desire for flight within him. The room confined him. It was mercifully dark and midnight. He dressed and left the house, walking swiftly, sometimes breaking into a run with the pressure and pursuit of agony. The streets of great London were deserted. He prowlèd them restlessly, seeking out the bridges of the Thames, standing upon them to watch the slow, gliding, unaffected pace of the river, shrinking down as though to blend himself into the very railings when a stranger passed by.

The secret that he had partly confessed to Charles Diodati, that he had nearly shown in far-off Rome, would now come out: the secret that he was afraid of women, that he felt uncertain of his ability to rule one in love and harmony, but to *rule,* as he and the age thought a man must do. There is no other secret with which malicious mankind will so torment his brother.

He knew that there was something wrong with this marriage, something lacking. He called it a lack in her and hated her for it. Yet he knew also that it was his own fault. He had refused to examine her nature while there was yet time. He had known the truth and refused to admit it. He had approved her with open eyes and had no right to find fault now with what he had chosen.

No man likes to realize that there is injustice in his attitude. Yet he saw that there was. It only made him hate himself and when a man hates himself, try as he may to punish himself, his aim is poor and most of his fury spills out on other people. Now, reason and blame himself as he might, his mutilated pride hated Mary Powell and burned with a plan for some fearful vengeance upon her.

Milton was one to strike back hard and quickly under any blow. A new heading appeared in his Commonplace Book: Divorce. The mishaps of personal life often drive a great man into the pathways of his boldest steps. Probably the subject would never have entered his mind but for his disappointment in his own marriage. No time was lost now. In August, 1643, John published the sensational pamphlet called *The Doctrine and Discipline of Divorce*.

Only a short time before, the Parliament had set up a system of censorship by requiring licenses for all published books or pamphlets. Such a system did not sit well with Milton so he defied it. His pamphlet was both unsigned and unlicensed. But if not signed it was from no fear of admitting to his views or evading the licensers. He polished and revised it, for it had been hastily penned. Then, with the addition of an address to Parliament, it was republished in February of 1644, openly signed, but again unlicensed.

Although it sprang from his own suffering it fitted into the pattern of his thought. He had launched a plea, beforehand, for religious liberty. Now he was crying out for liberty in personal life, several hundred years before his time.

Adultery was the only acknowledged ground for divorce. Moreover, for absolute divorce, enabling remarriage, a special act of Parliament was required. Who but the most wealthy could afford it? Milton argued that unsuitability of mind was quite the best reason for divorce. It is what the courts call "incompatibility" today, yet it is still not recognized in many places. Woman was made by God, he said, as the companion and partner of man. If this partnership were one of bitterness, loneliness, or hatred it could only result in evil for the married persons, the church, the state, and the children. Justice required that a man should be allowed to correct an innocent mistake. Shades of Mary Powell! There was just one little matter: he forgot to ask this liberty for women, too. It was the man, alone, for whom he asked this freedom when the wish to separate might be one-sided.

Suddenly, Milton found himself the center of a national scandal, written against and preached against. His character was blackened and defamed and the scandal of this divorce plea was to be kept alive by his political enemies until his dying day and used long afterward against his memory. He had truly dived headfirst into hot water.

The Presbyterians were now the most powerful faction in Parliament. When the divorce pamphlet appeared, a National Synod was meeting at Westminster, engaged in determining the religious forms for England now that the bishops were gone. Milton's lengthy argument, basing his belief in liberal divorce laws on scriptural texts, upset and outraged this assembly. They felt, moreover, that it was an intrusion upon their rights. These were matters they would settle.

He had been very popular with the Presbyterians when he wrote his eloquent pamphlets against the rule of bishops. Theirs was the form of church government he had endorsed. Now this friendship was at an end. A quarrel was begun between Milton and the Presbyterians which was to determine the course of his political career.

John was no longer the same. The Phillips boys, the young Lord Barrymore, Cyriack Skinner, and the other pupils of the school in Aldersgate found their master more stern and harsh than ever. Only slowly did he take up the threads of his friendships and begin to move back into the normal channels of his daily life. A rocklike firmness had set itself into the lines of his handsome, maturing face. The deceptive look of youth was gone. The lightness of the past May month was gone from the heart of Milton and would never come again.

Chapter 8

Oliver

B<small>ITTER</small> Royalist historians, in after years, told a story of how, at his uncle's estate of Hinchingbrooke, great confusion was caused one day when the infant Oliver Cromwell was discovered to be missing. A wild search of the house and grounds finally found the child on the very parapet of the roof, where he had been carried by a pet ape. So, they observed with sighs of regret, England was nearly rid of a monster. But the ape had been surefooted, the search had been lucky, and now the eyes of Englishmen, John Milton among them, were beginning to turn more and more upon Oliver Cromwell, whose name is pronounced "Crumwell."

This quiet, deeply religious, Puritan country gentleman had served in three parliaments. He had seldom opened his mouth to take part in debates. Not until the bold Long Parliament had come together to defy the King was his voice heard. When the "root and branch" measure was fought out he spoke his mind. For the first time most of his fellow members of the House of Commons took notice of him. Sir Philip Warwick, a King's man, remembered him well. "I came into the House one morning, well clad, and perceived a gentleman speaking whom I knew not, very ordinarily appareled, for it was a plain cloth suit, which seemed to have been made by an ill country tailor. His linen was plain, and not very clean; and I remember a speck or two of blood upon his little band, which was not much larger than his collar. His hat was without a hatband. His stature was of good size; his sword stuck close to his side; his countenance swollen and reddish; his voice sharp and untunable; and his eloquence full of fervor."

The fervor of Oliver's words rose from passionate belief. When the mild measure against bishops was finally adopted after midnight, by a close vote, Cromwell said, "Had it been rejected I would have sold tomorrow all I possess, and left England forever!" There might have been a new strong man in Massachusetts.

When the war broke out he was one of the first to act. The masters of Cambridge were about to obey the King's order to gather up for him their silver plate when, "down came Mr. Oliver Cromwell in a terrible manner, with what force he could gather together," and carried it off under their noses for the Parliament.

He was a man of courage and a superb horseman. His rank was not high in the army of Parliament, he merely commanded a company of cavalry, but as the war advanced his hand began to be felt throughout the army. Almost always the Parliament men were broken by the assault of the King's bold cavaliers. The army was too helter-skelter, made up of apprentices, broken-down servingmen, and halfhearted professionals. The devil-may-care cavaliers were brave and lusty fighters. They also believed devoutly in their cause so that only men with principles and convictions of their own could hope to beat them. The chaplain of Oliver's troops told how, "He had a special care to get religious men into his troop; these men were of greater understanding than common soldiers, and, making not money, but what they took to be public felicity to be their end, they were the more engaged to be valiant; for he that maketh money his end, doth esteem his life above his pay, and therefore is like enough to save it by flight, if he possibly can; but he that maketh the felicity of Church and State the end esteemeth it above his life and will the sooner lay down his life for it."

People jeered Oliver's notions. He would find few men of the kind he talked about, they said. "A few honest men," he replied, "are better than numbers." He began to recruit hand-picked troops. To everyone's astonishment a powerful force grew under his hand and continued to expand from 1643 to 1645, by which time this amazing army of Cromwell's was called the "New Model."

Then some members of Parliament complained that men from the lower stations of life were made captains in this outlandish New Model, whereas it was only fitting that born gentlemen should hold commands. Oliver paid no attention. "It provokes your spirit," he wrote to the Commons, "to see such plain men made captains of horse. It had been well that men of honor and birth had entered into their employments; but why do they not appear? But seeing it is necessary the work must go on, better plain men than none. I had rather have a plain russet captain who knows what he fights for, and loves what he knows, than what you call a gentleman and that is nothing else."

These men were of the same breed as those who built New England; loyal, upright in morals, passionate in conviction, fearless in the face of pain and death. Few armies have had such discipline. Some of the King's soldiers, who cursed so that they were called "Damn-me's," sneered at these troops among whom there was no drunkenness and no plundering and no coarse speech. It was Oliver's rule that "no man swears but he pays his twelvepence; if he is drunk he is set in the stocks or worse." This was a body of men worthy to meet in battle the gallantry of Charles's men.

All the same, there was another side to them. Many were ignorant men with deep resentments against what they did not understand. In some, bigoted convictions joined with the love for smashing and destruction to produce melancholy results. Their Puritan preachers told them that crosses, altars and altar vessels, handsome priestly vestments, lovely stained glass windows, ancient illuminated manuscripts, religious paintings and sculptures, were filthy Popish abominations. Thus, during the height of this Puritan revolution there was such a smashing, defacing, profaning, and destroying of all such things in many English churches that no man can make an accounting of the beauty destroyed, many times representing precious treasures of antiquity. Glorify it by what religious name the zealots might choose, it was barbarism.

From ancient parish churches in villages to Westminster Abbey in London the devastation of sacred art went on. There are records of payments made to one Thomas Stevens, with others, "for taking down the angels in the Abbey and cleansing out pictures." A Puritan writer named John Vicars wrote with pious satisfaction: "now the popish altar is quite taken away, the bellowing organs are demolisht, and pulled down . . . and for the gaudy, guilded crucifixes, and rotten rabble of dumb idols, popish saints and pictures, set up and placed, and painted thereabout, where that sinfull singing was used: now there is a most sweet assembly, and thicke throng of God's pious people. . . ."

The worst of these things followed the Puritan triumph, which Oliver's army had still to complete. But now his cavalry began to snatch victories out of battles that had begun to be defeats. The King's men learned to look sharply for him. One of the most successful field commanders of the royal forces was Charles' nephew, Prince Rupert, Duke of Bavaria, who had come to his uncle's aid and been given the rank of general of the horse. On the second of July, 1644, a great battle of the civil war was fought at Marston Moor. As Cromwell sat his horse at the edge of the field, waiting for the moment of action, his men brought him a soldier who had been a prisoner of the King's army. He had a message.

"Well?" asked Cromwell.

"Prince Rupert is there," the soldier said, pointing at the lines of the enemy. "He called me to him and asked, 'Is Cromwell there?' 'Yes,' I said to him. 'And will they fight?' he asks. 'Yes,' I said. 'Go to Cromwell,' he says, 'and tell him he shall have fighting enough.'"

Oliver stared across the moor. "If it please God, so shall he," he said.

When the battle was all but in Rupert's hand, Cromwell's relentless troop, sweeping in where his superiors had retreated, won the first major victory for the Parliament. Rupert, sitting weary and defeated among his own routed horsemen, stared back at the abandoned field where Cromwell was supreme. "Ironsides!" he said, in amazement, "Ironsides!" The great captain of horse had a name, now, that was to stick. "Ironsides," both he and his men, alike, were afterward called.

The position of Parliament was still none too strong. Among other things it was necessary to have the support of Scotland. The price exacted for this was that the new form of religion in England should be Presbyterian, after the Scottish system. Pym, the leader of Parliament, did not like the agreement but had to make it. The Presbyterian party was the strongest of the several in England and the treaty with the Scots made them supreme. They lost no time in drawing up strict rules of worship and picking quarrels with the smaller Protestant bodies.

Cromwell's soldiers included many members of independent religious groups. He woke up to the fact that the Parliament he was fighting for, through its Presbyterian leadership, was becoming as intolerant as the rule of bishops they had destroyed. The great Pym had just died and there was no other man of his stature in the House. Many men were beginning to feel that leadership would have to come, in time, from Cromwell who was still of no great official rank.

Oliver believed in toleration more than did most of the Parliament leaders. He had hand-picked these men of different faiths in his ranks and did not intend to see them persecuted by the men whose battles they were winning. One of his fellow officers proposed to discharge a lieutenant colonel because he was an Anabaptist. Cromwell spoke out vigorously. "Sir, the state in choosing men to serve it, takes no notice of their opinions. If they be willing faithfully to serve, that satisfies. Take heed of being sharp against those to whom you can object little but that they square not with you in every opinion concerning matters of religion."

Tolerance did not raise Cromwell's stock with Parliament. The leading Presbyterians of London announced, "We detest and abhor the much endeavored toleration." There were far too many Independents in London to suit their taste. When the Long Parliament had begun, there had even come a body of returned emigrants from New England, led by Hugh Peters, to take a hand in the new home struggle. The Presbyterians felt about the Independent groups as Bishop Hall had felt when he described them as rabble "instructed by guides fit for them, cobblers, tailors, feltmakers, and suchlike trash."

Yet Oliver's troubles were more than religious. Victories were won, but the war lagged. Those in high command of the armies of Parliament were afraid to win. This fear of victory began in Parliament itself. The army was prevented from organizing efficiently. Money for supplies and the pay of the troops was slow in coming. Cromwell fought and pleaded with Parliament for the means to supply his troops as George Washington was to do with Congress in the dark days of the American

Revolution. He protested to them, "Lay not too much upon the back of a poor gentleman who desires without much noise, to lay down his life, and bleed his last drop, to save the Cause and you." He spent most of his personal fortune on his troops, but it was a drop in the bucket.

The fear of victory was summed up by Lord Manchester, one of the commanders of the army. "If the King be beaten he will still be King; if he beat us he will hang us all for traitors." Cromwell's answer raised the hair on the heads of Parliamentary gentlemen. "If I met the King in battle," he declared, firmly, "I would fire my pistol at the King as at another."

Parliament removed Cromwell from battle by an act providing that none of its members should command in the field. But the King's forces mustered again. In a sudden panic, the House hastily sent Cromwell back to the army for one more stroke of work. He made it a good one.

On June thirteenth he rode into camp. The soldiers went wild with delight. "Ironsides!" they shouted. "Ironsides is here! Ironsides has come to lead us!"

The Battle of Naseby was fought next day against terrible odds. Cromwell smashed the King's forces once and for all. "Never have my affairs been in as good a state!" the King had rejoiced as the battle line drew up. Never had they been in a worse one afterward. Oliver said, "When I saw the enemy draw up and march in gallant order toward us, and we, a company of poor, ignorant men, to seek to order our battle, the general having commanded me to order all the horse, I could not, riding alone about my business, but smile out to God in praises, in assurance of victory, because God would, by things that are not, bring to naught things that are; of which I had great assurance, and God did it."

God, indeed, did it with a vengeance. Oliver that day ended the last possibility for absolute monarchy in England. He wrote his official report to Parliament, adding at its close, "Honest men served you faithfully in this action. Sir, they are trusty; I beseech you, in the name of God, not to discourage them. He that ventures his life for the liberty of his country, I wish that he trust God for the liberty of his conscience, and you for the liberty that he fights for."

Restless and unhappy days had fallen to John. The blessing of furious controversy kept him from sinking into moodiness and despair. He had a friend named Samuel Hartlib, a Pole, a man with broad ideas on education. With him the schoolmaster talked for long hours on the subject of teaching and training young men. John had never forgotten his scorn and hatred for the methods of Cambridge which, in his view, produced little more than pale, bishop-following clergymen unless a man had such strength of mind as to defy the system.

To Samuel Hartlib he addressed a short pamphlet setting in order the thoughts that had partly grown out of their talks and out of his own experience as a teacher. It sketched out an ambitious program of education. In contrast to the narrow, theological aims of the university, Milton said, "I call a complete and generous education that which fits a man to perform justly, skillfully and magnanimously all the offices, both private and public, of peace and war." "Only," he confesses at the end with a certain pride, "I believe that this is not a bow for every man to shoot in that counts himself a teacher."

The Presbyterians still cried out against his divorce pamphlet. His father, who had been shocked in the first place, urged him to drop the argument. "No," John insisted, "I will show them that it is not I alone who have preached such notions." He addressed directly to the clergymen a pamphlet called, *The Judgment of Martin Bucer concerning Divorce*. Bucer was a famous Protestant preacher whom King Edward

VI had brought from Germany to teach at Cambridge. Milton merely reprinted a section from Bucer's writings which upheld his divorce theories. It was impressive authority in that day and John insolently flaunted it in the face of the Presbyterians with the scriptural quotation, "Art thou a teacher in Israel and knowest not these things?"

They struck back at once. Milton had published his pamphlet with a license this time, as required by law. But they still had against him the first divorce pamphlet which had had no license. The stationer's company, whose duty was to carry out the licensing, launched charges against him. The Reverend Herbert Palmer preached a sermon to the Houses of Parliament and denounced the "ungodly toleration" that was in the air, singling out Milton as its worst example and urging that his books be burned.

When the charge was brought against him John went full swing into action. By November 25, 1644, he had finished his greatest prose work, *Areopagitica.* It took its name from the Areopagus, the hillside court of ancient Athens, upon which the accused and the accuser openly faced issues before all the people. He called it a "speech," "A Speech of Mr. John Milton for the Liberty of Unlicensed Printing, to the Parliament of England." It was published without a license.

No man has made a nobler plea for the freedom of the press than John Milton. He calls upon Parliament to reconsider its act requiring the licensing of books, as a mistake unworthy of it and unworthy of the nation. "Lords and Commons of England, consider what Nation it is whereof ye are, and whereof ye are the governors: a Nation not slow and dull, but of a quick, ingenious, and piercing spirit, acute to invent, subtle and sinewy to discourse, not beneath the reach of any point the highest that human capacity can soar to."

By the censoring of books only good books will suffer. Bad

books will find their way to the light anyway. But by free publishing the proper judgment of mankind can and will sort out the good from the evil. "To the pure all things are pure, not only meats and drinks, but all kinds of knowledge whether of good or evil; the knowledge cannot defile, nor consequently the books, if the will and conscience be not defiled." On the other hand, "as good almost kill a Man as kill a good Book; who kills a Man kills a reasonable creature, God's Image; but he who destroys a good Book, kills reason itself, kills the Image of God, as it were in the eye. Many a man lives a burden to the Earth; but a good Book is the precious life-blood of a master-spirit, embalmed and treasured up on purpose to a life beyond life. . . ."

Wherever books have been censored liberty has suffered and learning has been persecuted. He had seen this himself in Italy, he points out. "It was there that I found and visited the famous Galileo grown old, a prisoner to the Inquisition, for thinking in Astronomy otherwise than the Franciscan and Dominican licensers thought. And though I knew that England then was groaning loudest under the prelatical yoke, nevertheless I took it as a pledge of future happiness, that other Nations were so persuaded of her liberty."

He sings high praises of the new government of England and its destiny. It must be worthy of its past blows for liberty. "Believe it, Lords and Commons, they who counsel ye to such a suppressing, do as good bid ye suppress yourselves." If you debase the new liberty in such a way, he warns, you will find yourselves debased.

The Parliament must have the courage to face its bold destiny, for the greatest era of the world will lie ahead if it can do so. "Methinks I see in my mind a noble and puissant Nation rousing herself like a strong man after sleep, and shaking her invincible locks: Methinks I see her as an Eagle mewing her mighty youth, and kindling her undazzled eyes at the full mid-day beam; purging and unscaling her long-abused sight at the fountain itself of heavenly radiance; while the whole noise of timorous and flocking birds, with those also that love the twilight, flutter about, amazed at what she means."

The effects of *Areopagitica* are felt by us today. They were felt then, as well. The Parliament did not rise to his brave summons and the act was not repealed. But it could not well be enforced. Too many bold spirits answered the clear call of Milton and the licensers were defied as long as they existed.

History had another of its grim ironies to coincide with the completion of *Areopagitica*. Although Archbishop Laud had been in prison for some four years he was not forgotten. In that same November, Parliament passed a Bill of Attainder against him, as it had done four years earlier against Strafford, to make possible his execution, for there was no lawful case to condemn him. It was a member of Parliament with the oddly apt name of Mr. Harbottle Grimston, who cried vengefully: "We are now fallen upon the great Man the Archbishop of Canterbury. Look upon him as he is in Highness, and he is the Sty of all Pestilential filth . . . the great and Common Enemy of all Goodness and Good men." On the fourth of January, 1645, Laud's head fell.

In his faults and virtues he was all too like the Prince he served so closely. He was a reformer of the Church, but his reforms and those sought by the Puritans took drastically opposite directions, the one toward ancient catholic Christian tradition, the other toward separatist sectarianism, splintering into ever smaller bodies. Laud was high-tempered, as autocratic by nature as his monarch; his harshness was of the age he dwelt in, though the age justifies it in him no more than in his enemies.

A few months after this event, in 1654, Milton published two final pamphlets on divorce, *Tetrachordon* and *Colasterion*. The first of these contained a note that was alarming to his friends. If Parliament did not grant the freedom of easy divorce to which Milton felt he had shown that men were entitled, they would be responsible for the consequences. It sounded like the statement of a man prepared to make some rash move.

It was nearly two years since Mary had left him. The sting of humiliation was still sharp in the bitter force of his pamphlets. But in his heart the image had faded. Who, now, was Mary Powell but a girl who had spent a few nights under his roof as a stranger and then gone forever?

His heart still sought the consolation it had missed. The arguments and studies, the world of politics and civil war, the tasks of schoolmaster, the comradeship of his friends; all these things failed to wipe out the longing for a true life partner.

It seemed as if he might have found her. Before he knew it he had been drawn into a close and intimate friendship with Mildred Davis, the daughter of his friend Dr. Davis. Mildred was all things Mary had not been. If not so beautiful she was no less charming. She was a few years older than Mary and versed in everything to fit her for the comradeship of Milton. She painted, played, and sang. Latin, French, and Italian were at her command. The poets and scholars Milton read were read by her. The volumes on his bookshelves were no closed mysteries to her understanding.

Mildred had not been guiltless of scorn toward Mary Powell. She had let the girl sense that she looked down upon her for an unlettered chit. Some jealousy beset her that she had not set herself to catch this Milton, never suspecting he would slip away and capture some country lass. She was glad when Mary left and felt a secret, dangerous excitement.

Suddenly Milton seemed to see the girl for the first time face to face. This was what he wanted. Why could not this girl, whose talk delighted him with its wisdom and understanding, be with him always in his home and at his side? What claim had Mary Powell on him, what right to some misguided loyalty? Why should he not repudiate her publicly as his wife and claim the right to take another, in full defiance of the world's opinion?

Then Mildred Davis discovered a thing she had in common with Mary. She could be frightened by John Milton. Suddenly the exciting game she was playing with him loomed up into a terrifying challenge. John had made a decision. He always made decisions. It had grown in his mind as he wrote the *Tetrachordon*. He hinted at it there, and then with true Miltonic audacity, launched it openly. He urged Mildred Davis to marry him.

She shrank from the fierce daring of his proposal. The closest of their friends were stunned and shocked. What would they do with this Puritan who considered bigamy with calm determination? To John it seemed that if a man might be so bold as to challenge a king in the name of justice and liberty, he might as easily challenge an unjust law.

He found himself alone. No other spirit would venture so far. The young lady is hardly to be blamed if she did not love John Milton to the utmost defiance of the world. It was a great deal to ask. Respectability won. Again John was beaten. He failed to win a wife and lost a friend, for their relationship was compromised by the bold appeal and its refusal.

It was as well, for it was a fight he could not have won. Even in our day, when divorce is more accepted, the state will not encourage it, and while different branches of the Christian Church hold differing views, all regard the sacrament of Holy Matrimony as something not to be broken lightly to suit the wills of impetuous men or women. His career had already suffered for it. He was, by 1645, the leading writer of the Independent party. The Presbyterians often described it as the sect of Miltonists or divorcers.

John turned back alone to the fight. He wrote two sonnets to the attackers of his divorce pamphlets. One of them began with a lusty string of insults worthy of his rougher pamphlet style:

> I did but prompt the age to quit their clogs
> By the known rules of ancient liberty,
> When straight a barbarous noise environs me
> Of owls and cuckoos, asses, apes and dogs.

He lashes out at men

> That bawl for freedom in their senseless mood,
> And still revolt when truth would set them free.

Against the Presbyterians he flung the famous "tailed sonnet" (cast like a sonnet but with six extra lines): *On the New Forces of Conscience Under the Long Parliament*. Milton now regarded the Presbyterians as tyrants and turned away from them. It seemed to him that they had not hated but merely envied the tyranny of the bishops. Now they were oppressors in their turn. There was no difference between them and those they had overthrown. Now John hurled at them the charge that

> New Presbyter is but Old Priest writ large.

In the Street of St. Martin's le Grand was the house of a man named Blackborough, a relative of the Miltons. John had a friendly affection for him and paused there almost daily, as he passed upon his business.

One afternoon in August he stopped for a few words. Blackborough greeted him warmly, with a touch of nervousness in his manner.

"Well, what is it, Cousin?" Milton asked. "You look as though ill luck in business had befallen you."

"No, no, John. But there is something I would like you to see. Come in."

As Milton entered the house his kinsman excused himself. "Be good enough to go into my library," he begged. "I will join you there."

John entered the library, slightly curious at the air of mystery. The door was closed behind him as he crossed the room. Turning, he found himself facing Mary Milton.

The blood rushed hotly to his face. For once he could not command words for he did not know what he wished to say. The girl, who was now nineteen, had a more sober and saddened look than when he had seen her last. She was still lovely, but bitterness flooded over the memory of his affection.

Mary seemed keyed to a high pitch of effort. She was frightened and did not know what outburst she might expect. The pamphlets her husband had written had horrified her. She had shrunk from the whispers of scandal and denunciation they had swirled about her since she bore his name. But fear had entered the Powell family after Cromwell's victory at Naseby. They were pinched for money and the King was losing. Pride must be swallowed. They had better pack their daughter back to her Parliament husband as a dike against the rising flood.

"Mr. Milton," she said, hesitantly, "I will come back."

"Indeed!" he snapped, with more harshness than he had intended.

A flicker of fear passed across her face. Humiliation followed it. He repented of his tone and spoke again.

"Madam," he asked quietly, "what reason have I to receive you again? Or what reason have you to come to me?"

"Let me be honest, Mr. Milton," she said. "There is no place for me to go. It may go ill with my family. I have been undutiful as a wife. I cannot help myself if you refuse me. But if you will have me back again I shall know my duty toward you."

John's pride was great, so great that it did not like the sight of a humbled pride before it. He did not know what to say. He was cornered, being forced to a decision he did not wish to make. What did he owe this girl? Was it his heart or his pride that hardened against her?

"It is a late hour for mending, Mistress Milton," he said, uncertainly. "It is two years since we have spoken. Can it be prudent for us to join our hands again?"

"You must ask yourself," she said, "for I can do nothing else."

"How do you come to be here?"

"It was my aunt arranged it, through the kindness of Mr. Blackborough, whom I hope you will not blame. I feared you would not consent to see me, otherwise."

"You were no doubt right," he said.

They were silent. Something of pity stirred in John. He did not wish it so and turned his mind from it. He had followed impulses to a miserable end before. He must not do so again.

"It is clear," he said at last, "that you come to me of a sort of near necessity. I cannot ask if there is any affection that also draws you for I feel that it could not be so after what has passed. I feel that there could have been no such quality left within you when you took such abrupt leave of me. You claim lodging with me, therefore, on the strength of those lawful bonds which my printed words have done nothing to loosen. The question seen in this way, madam, is one I cannot answer at once. I will give you my answer tomorrow."

He turned to go toward the door, beyond which the troubled Blackborough waited. Mary swayed slightly as he moved from her. "Wait," she cried, as his hand was upon the door.

John turned. The girl ran forward and seized his hand, gazing into his face. If not love, there was a strange mixture of awe and respect in her troubled eyes. "Forgive me," she said, softly.

Milton gently freed his hand and met her gaze for a moment. Then he left the room.

Throughout a troubled night he wrestled with this unforeseen problem. Somehow it had seemed unreal that he should ever be faced with this girl again. The thought that haunted him was his defeat. His pamphlet notwithstanding, there was no divorce for him under the circumstances. This was imprisonment. When Mildred Davis had recoiled from his proposal he had seen the wildness of his rebellious impulses. He was trapped. So, on the other hand, was Mary. If it was necessity rather than love that had brought her back it was at least an honest basis. He did not want her back. But he could not make up his mind to cast her off in the face of her appeal. He needed a wife. He needed a woman's companionship. The hatred he thought he had nursed for her had proved a weak thing. Perhaps the faith in tolerance that he held in matters of public life could be turned in private life to mend this ugly breach. Conscience would not permit him to refuse.

The next day he sent word to Mary that she might return. There was no longer room enough at Aldersgate Street, with the growth of the school. For a short while he took lodgings for her at the home of the Widow Webber. Meanwhile he prepared to move. In September the Milton household moved into Barbican Street. It was not far. It was a larger but less attractive house, in a narrower street. Here Mary took up, once more, the duties of housewife.

John had little enough time to think about his decision and question it. He was correcting proofs of the first edition of the *Poems of Mr. John Milton, both English and Latin, composed at several times. Printed by his true copies.*

Milton's name was widely known in London. It was an irony that few people realized that he was a poet. Humphrey

Moseley, the publisher of the volume, explained in a preface that he knew that pamphlets were more profitable these days than works of art. He published them, therefore, out of love for the English language, in pride at introducing the truest poet after Spenser.

John's eyes smarted and troubled him as he studied the proof pages. He felt he had strained them in the concentrated effort of the pamphlets. They pained him somewhat, when tired, and the candle flame, in the evening, seemed to take on a haze of colors around it.

Then his pride still worried him on the question of his wife. In the eyes of the world, was her return a victory for him or a defeat? He was never able to make up his mind.

Oliver's troubles were only beginning. When he had crushed the King's forces at Naseby, Charles had escaped. The desperate monarch knew not where to turn. At last he went to Scotland and gave himself up in the hope that the Scots would feel some loyalty toward a king who was of Scottish blood. But the Scots remained true to their alliance and delivered Charles over to the army of Parliament.

The strain between the army and Parliament was growing worse. "Toleration was the devil's masterpiece," the Presbyterians claimed, while most of their victories had been won for them by Independents. Parliament hoped to make a deal with the King with Presbyterianism as its basis. To prevent a double cross the army refused to deliver up Charles to the agents of Parliament and held him for themselves.

Charles was well pleased with this state of affairs. He wrote to one of his friends. "I am not without hope that I shall be able to draw either the Presbyterians or the Independents to side with me for extirpating one another, so that I shall be really King again." If his armies had failed him his wits had not.

Nothing is more difficult than to tear down completely some long-established machinery of government. This was where the strength of the King lay. Every step away from him grew more difficult than the last one, while to make peace with him seemed so simple and easy a way back to order. And so it might have been if there had been any least bit of yielding in the King. But Charles would make no real agreement. Any promise he made to either side was merely a step on his way back to where he had started from—absolute monarchy. Even Cromwell and the army had not yet realized how determined the King could be. They would restore him if he would promise toleration. In his talks with Cromwell he appeared so sincere that Oliver called him "the uprightest and most conscientious man of his three kingdoms."

There was no hope of toleration from Parliament. Many army men were for marching on London and asserting their will forcibly. Oliver counseled against it, fervently. They should still try to negotiate with the Houses. "Whatsoever we get by a treaty, whatsoever comes to be settled upon us that way, will be firm and durable, and will be conveyed over to posterity. That will be the greatest honor to us that ever poor creatures had. We shall avoid the great objection that will be against us, that we have got things of the Parliament by force. Things though never so good, obtained in that way, it will exceedingly weaken the things both to us and to all. Really, really, have it what you will, that which you have by force, I look upon it as nothing."

The army professed a high-minded program. It desired only justice and the toleration of religious beliefs. It did not even wish to destroy the Presbyterial form of government. But there were petty, shortsighted men in Parliament who would yield nothing. They wanted to disband the army and then crush all Independent beliefs.

In November, 1647, the King escaped. He fled to the Isle of

Wight and was captured again. At once he renewed his plots, this time mostly with Parliament. Certain elements in Scotland sided with him, on his promise this time to enforce Presbyterianism, and an insurrection broke out against the army. A second civil war, which Cromwell had desperately sought to avoid, was now beginning; this time almost a war between the army and Parliament.

Oliver had cried out, "The hour is come for the Parliament to save the kingdom and to govern alone." But Parliament had no such republican notions. It supported the new Scottish insurrection. The King would back up its intolerant Presbyterianism. It passed the terrible "Ordinance for the Suppression of Blasphemies and Heresies," passed it by an immense majority. This was as bad as anything of Bishop Laud's. It threatened imprisonment and death for anti-Presbyterian heresies.

Sadly and bitterly the army took up the new fight. The night before they marched into action its leaders passed a solemn resolution which showed the hopelessness of dealing, now, with either King or Parliament: "That it was our duty, if ever the Lord brought us back again in peace, to call Charles Stuart, that man of blood, to account for the blood he has shed and mischief he has done to his utmost against the Lord's cause and people in this nation."

The insurrection did not last long. Early in October, 1648, Cromwell entered Edinburgh and the war was about over. Oliver took no vengeance on the Scots. The King's threat ended, he left them to themselves. They were mostly Presbyterians and could remain so, dealing with Scottish Roman Catholics themselves. It was their right. He had no wish to be an oppressor in his turn. His attitude is shown in a letter written after his victory. "I profess to thee I have desired from my heart, I have prayed for it, I have waited for the day to see wiser and right understanding between the godly people, Scots, English, Jews,

Gentiles, Presbyterians, Independents, Anabaptists and all. Our brethren of Scotland were our greatest enemies. God hath justified us in their sight, caused us to requite good for evil."

Parliament learned nothing from this generous example. The Presbyterians stuck to their intolerance. Things were not slow to happen. On November thirtieth the army again seized Charles who was still on the Isle of Wight hopefully watching the insurrection. The army leaders in London determined that Parliament would have to be reckoned with. On December sixth, Colonel Thomas Pride entered the Parliament with a band of troops. He arrested some forty Presbyterians and turned out of the House some hundred more. After "Pride's Purge," as the deed became known, there were only fifty or sixty members left seated. These were promptly dubbed the "Rump Parliament."

Cromwell had had no part in the purge and had not known about it in advance. He could do nothing but approve it, for the deadlock had been hopeless.

"By what right do you act?" a member had demanded of Colonel Pride. Hugh Peters, the returned emigrant from New England, replied, "By the right of the sword." Oliver had said, "that which you have by force I look upon it as nothing." Now, true Parliamentary rule was ended by the purest force under the purest necessity. Dismayed and troubled, Oliver took his seat in the Rump Parliament.

Chapter 9

"Sad Stories
of the Death of Kings"

THE HOUSE in Barbican Street became a kind of Noah's Ark in June of 1646. Oxford, the last stronghold of the King's broken forces, had fallen to Lord General Fairfax. Squire Powell was ruined. He had barely enough influence to get a safe-conduct for himself and his family to London. Thither they went, with nothing but a meager cartload of personal possessions, to take the refuge they had prudently assured themselves by sending Mary back to her lawful husband.

John and Mary had made a go of things in the past year. Although companionship such as he had longed for, and romance such as she had dreamed of, were denied to each of them, enough of respect and familiar, day-to-day affection existed to keep the household smooth between them. Now they were expecting a child within a month. John kept muffled within himself an intense longing that it should be a son.

When the refugees from Forest Hill came straggling in, Milton's whole soul cried out to turn them away, which was a thing he could not do. The squire was loud and lavish with a sudden new affection and esteem for his son-in-law. "You fooled us all, you fooled us all," he said with admiration. "You got yourself on the right side from the beginning. You're a shrewd man, more's the credit to you."

Mistress Powell had always disliked him, with much more than a mere mother-in-law's distaste. Disaster had not sweetened her acid nature. She looked on Milton not as a rescuer but as an added curse.

Three sons, Robin, Harry, and Dick were with them. These five souls must be added to the house already containing John, Mary, old Mr. Milton, and the Phillips boys. It was not a quiet gathering. The squire fumed and fussed over the preparing of lawsuits, in the vain hope of fishing some salvage from the general wreck. He pumped the old scrivener for advice and poured out his monarchist woes to an unsympathetic ear. Mrs. Powell nagged and worried over Mary, who was nervous already with the coming child. The Phillips boys mixed badly with the Powell boys and loud voices were raised ten times within an hour.

John and his father clung together like shipwrecked sailors on a hostile shore. The nature of the house had changed at once. The peace of quiet scholarship was banished. It was an ordeal to conduct the morning classes with the hum of wrangling voices in the background, sometimes rising to a loud outcry.

On the twenty-ninth of July the child arrived. It was a girl. Intense disappointment struck John as the news was given at the bedroom door. Still, he was excited. It was a child, flesh of his flesh. Perhaps he might raise up, with this child and others that would no doubt follow, the comforting companions he had vainly sought to have around him. It was a large emotion to become a father, even to an austere, heretical, Puritan agitator.

When the midwife had gone, John came and stood alone beside the bed of his wife. He had shooed the other members of the family from the room with a firm hand. He looked down, now, at the tired girl and the child swaddled beside her.

"Well, Mary," he asked kindly, "what shall we name the child?"

"What should you like to name her?" She smiled at him.

"It would be pleasant to call her Anne, after my sister," Milton suggested.

Mary considered, then smiled again, with a sly joke. "It is a good name. We could also call her Anne, after my mother."

John laughed. "That is a wise thought," he admitted; "that may buy a wealth of good will. We will call her Anne. Let all who wish feel honored."

In spite of the christening, harmony did not rule the house. Mrs. Powell sought to rule it and succeeded in all the spheres where John took no active part. To him, when the first flush of fatherhood was past, it merely seemed as though a constant wailing had added itself to the maddening noises of the family. The child was sickly and cried almost continuously. At times, distracted and wrought up over his books and papers, he cried out in despair against the horde that threatened to engulf him.

It thinned out in time. The squire's health began to fail. "I won't be long among you," he began to prophesy, dolefully. "I feel that my time is coming." To be near the squire was to discount all he said. But the hint of death was true and others felt it as he failed. It was no windbag rambling that set him on this theme.

Old Mr. Milton, still the scrivener, helped the squire draw his will, to provide his children with legacies of lost property. On the first day of the new year, 1647, Richard Powell died.

The real blow, for John, was reserved for two months more. Then, in the middle of March, Mr. Milton died suddenly and was buried in St. Giles, Cripplegate. John's grief for the gentle old man was great. He had blessed his son richly with good parenthood and loyal support. He had endowed him with the early love of art and learning and supported him with worldly goods. The long years had ripened their affection. His death left John with no true, understanding spirit to share his house with him. He was lonely in his crowded home, though John and Edward Phillips, who were fast maturing, gave him some companionship.

A letter came from Carolo Dati, the closest of his Florentine friends. It showed that three other letters had missed their way before it, and the little fact struck John sadly, with a sense of loss out of all keeping with its real importance. He lost no time in answering his friend, speaking of his desolation.

"Those whom the mere necessity of neighborhood, or something else of a useless kind, has closely conjoined with me, whether by accident or by the tie of law, *they* are the persons, though in no other respect commendable, who sit daily in my company, weary me, nay, by heaven, all but plague me to death whenever they are jointly in the humor for it, whereas those whom habits, disposition, studies, had so handsomely made my friends, are now almost all denied me, either by death or by most unjust separation of place, and are so for the most part snatched from my sight that I have to live well-nigh in a perpetual solitude."

He could stand matters only a few months more. The Powells were intolerable. Mary, herself, had no joy of their presence in the house. Barbican Street had not been the most pleasant of homes and now it had sad memories. At the end of the summer John made financial arrangements for Mrs. Powell and moved her, with her sons, into a separate dwelling. Then, with his reduced household, he moved, in October, to the neighborhood of High Holborn. The house was pleasing, though smaller than the previous ones. It was farther into the city by some distance but backed upon Lincoln's Inn Fields, with its park and bowling green, in a section of new houses.

Here, a year later, a second daughter, Mary, was born to the Miltons. John gave up hope for a son.

To Oliver Cromwell, one of his fellow members of Parliament had one time said, "If you prove not an honest man, I will never again trust a fellow with a great nose." Events were now shaping to put the integrity of great noses to a hard test.

What was to be done with the ever-treacherous King? The army had already passed a resolution that he must be punished. The Rump Parliament now had to take up the question. The majority, with whom Oliver threw in his voice, were for bringing Charles to trial.

Sir Harry Vane, and some other leading figures, disagreed. They argued that there was no law under which to try a King. If there were none, the others argued, then the Parliament would have to constitute itself such an authority and appoint a commission for the purpose. Cromwell retorted angrily to the fainthearted. Once he had said he would fire his pistol at the King as at any other. Now, he said, "I tell you we will cut off his head with the crown on it." Many strong men fell back from this awful decision. Oliver was a man slow to choose his course. But when, in all conscience, he had decided, he would face any consequence.

On the first of January, 1649, the Parliament named a court of one hundred fifty men to try the King. John Bradshaw was its chairman. Some refused to serve, but the work was begun. It was January twentieth when Charles was brought before his judges. The trial dragged out for five days. Charles defied and denounced the court. He would not recognize its right to try him and would not testify before it. There was no law, he affirmed—and he was right—by which this Parliament could bring a King of England to trial. "It is not my case alone," he insisted, "it is the freedom and liberty of the people of England." Again, ironically, he was right. But he had damaged that freedom himself. He had not used the sharp intelligence with which he mocked the legal pretensions of Parliament in wise moderate rule that would have kept these men from rising against him in exasperation. Yet in spite of the King's failures the freedom and liberty of the English people lay in the rule of valid law and the legitimate transition of power. These were now being violated and good could not come from it. But the trial proceeded and sentence of death was passed upon the King.

A scaffold was set up at Whitehall. On January thirtieth a vast crowd of anxious people saw their King march boldly up to his masked executioners. He would die well. Calmly he asked God that his enemies might be forgiven, even those who had brought him to this pass. He knelt at the headsman's block. There were scattered cries of "God save the King!" and as the royal head fell, in spite of the grim Roundhead troops surrounding the scaffold and the crowd, a witness recorded, "there was such a groan by the thousands then present as I never heard before and desire I may never hear again."

Thus he died—neither the villain the Puritans would make him nor the saint his martyrdom to a principle made him to the royalists. In Sir Winston Churchill's words, he "had resisted with . . . untimely stubbornness the movement of his age."

Many English hearts were dismayed by this deed. It was charged, and it was true, that the greater number of the English people were not in support of it. It was the Puritan leaders and the Presbyterian party in Parliament who had done it, consequences be what they might.

The Parliament declared that the prosecution of Charles was "to the end that no chief officer, or any magistrate whatsoever, may hereafter pursue tortuously or maliciously to imagine or contrive the enslaving or destroying of the English nation, and to expect impunity for so doing." As a celebrated English judge observed to the convicted thief before him, "You are being hanged not for stealing a horse, but that horses may not be stolen."

To one of his friends, Oliver wrote, "Be not offended at the manner. Perhaps there was no other way left."

This was the opinion of Milton. During the period of the trial he had been at work upon a new pamphlet. He was the first prominent Englishman, outside of the Parliament, to support the killing of the King and to call for a republic. Two weeks after Charles's head had fallen he published *The Tenure of Kings and Magistrates,* "Proving," as a long subtitle declared, "that it is lawful, and hath been held so through all ages, for any, who have the power, to call to account a Tyrant, or wicked King, and after due conviction, to depose, and put him to death; if the ordinary Magistrate have neglected, or denied to do it. And that they who of late so much blame deposing, are the men that did it themselves."

It has been said that this was equal, on Milton's part, to adding his name to those upon the death warrant of the King. It was a fearless, uncompromising stand.

Four days before *The Tenure of Kings and Magistrates* was published a little book came into circulation from the underground supporters of the monarchy, who had lost no time rallying to the banner of the late King's son, now Charles II. This was the *Eikon Basilike,* or *Royal Image,* more popularly known as the "King's Book." It was to become the fantastic best seller of its time, spreading in scores of editions, of different sizes and shapes, throughout England, Scotland, and the Continent.

The book was supposed to represent the prayers, meditations, and observations of the "martyred" King in the last days before his execution. It was a tearjerker of the first class, skillfully aimed at the broadest level of popular sentiment. Only one conclusion could be drawn from its noble and moving pages—the dead King must have been an angel walking among men. It implied the deepest blackness in the hearts of those who had "murdered" him. The real author of the book was the Reverend John Gauden, an ingenious Presbyterian minister.

The guiding body of the present government was the Council of State. Among its members were President Bradshaw, Oliver Cromwell, Lord Thomas Fairfax, and Sir Harry Vane. The backward road was closed to them by the execution. The road ahead was hard. Complex diplomatic problems lay ahead of them in securing recognition from the governments of Europe. Drastic changes of government in one country frighten established governments in others—who may be reluctant to recognize the change.

In its diplomatic problems the new government needed a Secretary for Foreign Tongues, or Latin Secretary, since most international affairs were managed in this language. John Milton's name had led the list of those writing in the cause of freedom for several years. With his latest stroke, in *The Tenure of Kings and Magistrates,* it was not surprising that the Council of State should think of him. On Tuesday, March thirteenth, two members of the council called upon the poet-schoolmaster-pamphleteer and offered him the post, at an excellent salary.

John was unprepared for such an invitation. It startled and upset him, as well as flattered him. Was he now to enter officially into the world of politics? Were the working drafts of the poet to be buried under sheaves of state papers? He hesitated. He would give an answer when he could, he told them.

Two days later there was a knock at the door in Holborn. Milton, alone at the time, answered it. In his cloudy sight there stood a dark-clothed man, of large frame. Blinking and peering, knowing for a moment only that it was a stranger, John then discerned a coarse-textured, inflamed-looking face, a prominent nose. The voice that inquired, "Mr. Milton?" was low-timbred, with a husky rasp.

Then, at once, John knew it was Oliver Cromwell who stood before him, even before the caller supplied the name, modestly. Recognition had been slowed not only by poor sight, but by the startling unexpectedness of the visit.

"Come in, General Cromwell. You do me honor and take me by surprise."

Cromwell was not even President of the Council but that his presence was of great weight in it was certain. He sat, as his host requested, and for a prolonged moment there was silence between the man of war and the man of words.

"You have hesitated, Mr. Milton, at the proposed post of Secretary for Foreign Tongues?"

Milton had not collected his thoughts. He answered in a fashion to hold off the question.

"It is true that I read, write, and speak when I must, the principal European tongues. I would not wish to write in French; that language and the thought that floats on it are not congenial to my mind."

Cromwell was not a smiling man, but his formidable face relaxed into good humor. "Latin is as much your tongue as though you had been foster-mothered like Romulus and Remus by the Roman wolf. Call it Latin Secretary—for that is not only the language of the scholar, and the brawling pamphleteers, it serves sufficiently for matters of state in any nation. It will be seen that the new governors of this land have high learning at their call. You will do us honor."

Let him know the truth, Milton had decided, as his visitor spoke.

"General, my vocation, the calling ordained for me, is poet. Already I have betrayed it by that spirit in me that draws me whether I will or not into debate and controversy—pamphlet brawls as you say. But to do this in office, to pledge myself, to write on call. . . ."

"All ages have their poets," Cromwell said, not at home on this ground, "but some ages have crying need for the brawler. Pardon me, I mean the term with honor. I am myself a brawler with iron and steel. But the soldier cannot do all. The man with the quill is essential."

"This translation of state papers is a drudgery," Milton protested. "We are not a people poor in scholars. This work could be done by many."

"There are many who can translate," Cromwell countered, "but there are not many whose names, when it is known that they are the translators, would themselves add a lustre to the words. Also the words of state require both the sharpest precision and the finest subtlety, the mere gross meaning is not enough."

Milton was flattered. The General, whether he knew poets or not, did know men, and was aware of it.

"I know no reason I should come to you," he went on. "There is no special claim I can make. But you have written as one drawn inescapably into the outer precincts of these grim events, as I have acted as one drawn inescapably to the heart of them. There is that parallel, however faint it seem. What is wanted of you is not just to render clearly to other nations the policies of the Council. We need such a voice and mind as yours to defend us and speak for us—even to attack for us—against those influential attackers to whom we, as a Council, cannot address ourselves as we can to ambassadors and princes. These are not things which we can tell you to say, but things that you can say in your own thought and words for us better than any other man in England."

Milton, who also knew when he was flattered and could guard against it, now was touched more powerfully. He was challenged, too. That was the hardest of all things to resist. When he spoke again, he knew he was yielding.

"I told the other Councillors who waited on me that my sight is weakening." It was a fact that his eyes bothered him increasingly. The doctors did not know what to do for him. Lately the left side of his left eye had blacked out leaving only half its range of vision. The figure of his visitor swam mistily before him now. Writing and printing had to be held close to his face for him to make it out. Long sessions of work were painful and led to increasing smokiness in his sight. He said all these things and added, "It is not only that I question my ability to carry added burdens, but I must conserve and husband this waning light."

Cromwell seemed almost unmoved. "We give what we must," he said, with the matter-of-factness of the man who stakes his life in battles. He was needed, the General said again. He urged Milton to accept; it could be managed, he was sure. If necessary, assistance could be found to save him the drudgery. "It is the mind we need, more than hand or eye." Could they count on him?

"I will do it," Milton said, after a pause. He spoke slowly, with heavy spirit, but spoke again. "I will do it."

Four days later, the institution of monarchy was abolished by the Parliament. After two months more, in May, the commonwealth was brought into existence. "The people of England and of all the dominions and territories thereunto belonging are, and shall be, and are hereby constituted, made, established, and confirmed, to be a commonwealth and free state, and shall henceforth be governed as a commonwealth and free state by the supreme authority of this nation, the representatives of the people in parliament, and by such as they shall appoint and constitute officers and ministers for the good of the people, and that without any king or house of lords."

John had busied himself with his new job. He must be daily at Whitehall, now, at the council sessions. High Holborn was too far away. He moved his household temporarily to nearby Charing Cross. The council had promised to find official quarters for him, in time.

Mary complained a little at the moving. She had moved too often. The whole thing was hard for her to understand. The routine of the house had changed. There had been no more schoolteaching, now, for some time. Ned Phillips was preparing for Oxford and would soon be gone. John Phillips was serving his uncle as a sort of secretary. It was a lot to swallow. The young Mistress Milton had been shocked at the free talk against the King when first she married. Now her husband was called one of the King killers and was a part of the rebel government.

John was daily in the company of the men who were fulfilling England's destiny. His voice was heard among them and his hand and mind were tools in their workings. His tasks were big and little; letters had to be penned in Latin to foreign courts, other letters or documents must be translated into English that some members of the council might understand them. Speeches or pamphlets must be written in reply to the growing number of attacks upon the government. The old licensing act was dead, but a new censorship, strictly political, was needed now. There were suspected papers to be studied and reported upon. All in all, the tasks were many. There was beginning the steady flow of state papers in flawless Latin that were to impress suspicious foreign governments with the scholarship and culture of the new English rulers.

The Royalist propaganda was alarmingly good. A sensational pamphlet had come out of Holland in May, just about the time when the commonwealth was proclaiming itself. The

King's men had spared nothing. They had got themselves the services of the leading Latin scholar of Europe, the Frenchman Claude de Saumaise, better known by the Latin name of Salmasius. He had written *Defensio regia pro Carolo I* ("Defense of King Charles I"). It made a deep impression both in England and in Europe.

Meanwhile, something must be done about the King's Book. The notion that Charles was a virtuous martyr was becoming far too popular. The secretary was instructed to prepare an answer to it.

This was not the best of tasks for John. The appeal of the King's Book was to the people. A rebuttal, to do any good, would also have to reach the people. As a pamphleteer it was Milton's weakness that he wrote for the few, for the scholars. The Reverend John Gauden had him at a disadvantage.

John knew quite well that Charles had not written the book. It was necessary, however, to accept the popular belief that he had done so. He called his answer *Eikonoklastes,* the *Image Breaker,* in reply to *Eikon Basilike,* the *Royal Image.* The violent, not always just and well-considered, style that Milton used, especially on subjects not too close to his heart, was a bad antidote for the superhumanly meek and virtuous spirit of the King's Book of prayer and devotion. We can be tainted by the weapons we use. Milton, accepting the standards of harsh controversy, sank below himself to abuse, vulgarity, misrepresentation—even lies—to parody the King so praised by his opponent.

The more Milton denounced the King and praised the Parliament the more he failed to cut at the strength of *Eikon Basilike.* In one year the King's Book ran to forty-seven editions. In three years *Eikonoklastes* ran to three. Still, he had praised the government highly and the Council was satisfied. The King's

Book had been a master stroke. Little could be done about it by anyone.

In November, Milton was given comfortable and roomy apartments in Whitehall. The family lived in dignity in the palace of the Tudors. Mary was overawed but proud. She was carrying a third child, now, who would be born into an illustrious home. It would be fitting for this to be the longed-for boy.

Chapter 10

"Dark, Dark, Irrecoverably Dark"

O N THE FLYLEAF of his big Bible the hand of Milton wrote, "My son John was born on Sunday March the sixteenth about half an hour past nine at night, 1650." "My" was characteristic of the man, as if his son had no mother but had sprung from his brow like Athena from Zeus's in the myth.

It was the day following. He put down the pen and closed this family record that now bore its greatest tidings. In the bedroom Mary lay, weakly. It had gone hard with her. John went back in and sat beside her. Little Anne and Mary, now four and two years old, respectively, played out in the parks of the Tudors under the watchful eye of a servant. John Phillips was busily writing at the table, with a pile of Milton's official letters.

The house was quiet and contented. John smiled with tenderness and spoke gently to his wife who, with the blessing of God upon them, had now brought him the son he had awaited. She smiled in turn but was too weak to answer him.

It was past midnight, some weeks later, when Mary awoke with a start. She slept with a mother's lightness, tuned to the least outcry of the new infant. But it was not the child that she had heard. Her hand fumbled with the candle and tinder. The weak light flickered up. Her husband was sitting up in the bed, his palms pressed to his eyes, a sort of despair in his posture.

"What is it, John?" He did not answer her at once. Alarmed, she put out her hand and touched his shoulder. "What is it?"

He seemed suddenly to arouse from a deep reverie.

"I cannot sleep," he said, dully.

"Is it your eyes? Do they pain you?"

"It's not pain," he said, "it is the lights."

"But there is no light except the candle."

"There is a sort of lightning in my brain. In the daylight or even now, with the candle lit, I am all right. But in the darkness, when my eyes are closed, there are lights that flare and flash or drift in spots across my eyes."

"Oh, please, please, John," she begged, in distress, "go again to Dr. Paget tomorrow. Surely he can help you. He must."

"There is little I can get from him but good friendship, I am afraid," John said, quietly. "Do you go to sleep, Mary. If I cannot do the same, why, then, I shall watch out the night."

He went once more to Nathan Paget, on the next morning.

"Well, John," the physician greeted him, "what is it? New symptoms with the eyes?"

"Yes, Nathan, and I fear you will be no more help to me than a confessor. I can comfort myself with telling you of my troubles, but what, then, will you do for me?"

"What is it now?"

"There are lights at night, when my eyes are closed in the darkness. They startle me into wakefulness and mar my rest. Then I am vexed at my work by a trick of the left eye. With such narrow vision as is left in it all objects seem smaller than to the right eye. It is a lack of balance and agreement that strains me to great nervousness. In both my eyes, Nathan—and you do not know the fear with which I tell it to you—in both eyes the world is fading from me. I am becoming wrapped in mists."

Dr. Paget shook his head. "I am powerless, John, powerless. I know the limits of my narrow science. There are some men in Europe who might claim to help you, but I doubt them. Not much is known about this wondrous thing, the eye. When God wills to close it there is little to be done."

The pamphlet of Salmasius defending Charles I had done much harm to the commonwealth, at home and especially abroad. "Lay aside everything else," the council urged John, "and answer it with so strong a blast as to silence it in England and everywhere."

It was a big job and John went at it thoroughly and deliberately. He felt a powerful responsibility in the task. The supporters of Charles II were warring on the Commonwealth in Ireland and Scotland. Cromwell was struggling to put down these foes while Europe watched anxiously.

The General had sailed on his Irish expedition soon after his call on Milton. It was as if, cloaked under his words, there had been some foresight of what he felt must be done in Ireland and the knowledge that he would need a strong defender. His war against the late King's followers in Roman-Catholic Ireland —a war unsparingly extended to all the people—was waged with a ruthless cruelty that became a lasting memory to haunt Irish feelings toward England for centuries. What Milton thought of this is not known—or what he knew of it—but know what he may or think what he might, he was committed past question. The action fever to crush an adversary was no less intense in him than in Cromwell. His foe Salmasius, with learned persuasiveness, denounced the government of England as a pack of murderers whom other governments should band together to put to the sword. The respect and sympathy of the world were sorely needed.

The answer must not be written hastily. He began with a course of studies. Day after day was spent, searching the Scriptures and the classical writers, both religious and worldly, for arguments and weapons. To the licentious Roman comedies of

Plautus he turned to find new and pungent insults and abusive phrases of coarse grain to fling at his enemy. He would do this job in the grand, rough-and-tumble manner of the day, that odd combination of learned discourse and gutter brawl. He had assigned himself the better part of a year to do his work.

Dr. Paget saw the grind at which he worked and became alarmed. "Look here, John," he warned, "this will mean the end of your eyes, absolutely. I forbid it. I think, in fact, you should resign your secretaryship. You'll be a blind man in a year."

"John Phillips helps me," Milton said, apologetically. "It is a duty that I cannot shirk."

John Phillips helped, indeed, reading by the hour to save the painful straining of his uncle's eyes. But it could not all be done so. The work would go too slowly. Grimly, Milton plowed ahead. If it cost him his eyes, then it would cost them. Others had given their lives.

In the wakeful night hours, troubled by the false sensations of light, his spirit sometimes weakened and nakedly admitted its fear. He had a stout heart and could face many things boldly. But to be a blind man! Not to see! To fumble through his days in snail-like creeping led by indifferent or unwilling hands! Not to scan the pages of well-loved words. To be dependent on the halting tongues of unskilled readers, the flight of soaring thought grounded by uncomprehending middlemen; dull, uninterested minds to come between him and his springs of spiritual nourishment. And worst of all, henceforth to distill the strong brew of his own mind through the diluted ink of hired pens!

If, as is probable, Milton was suffering from the disease known as glaucoma, it made no vital difference that he did his work. The end was inevitable. The splendor of his determination is not weakened, for he did not know this. His blindness was then a mystery. We can only suppose its causes. Someone called it, "the condition in which the patient sees nothing and the doctor also sees nothing."

At the beginning of 1651, the answer to Salmasius was finished. It was published by William Dugard, a former Royalist printer whom Milton had visted in Newgate prison and persuaded to the Parliament's side. The title was *Joannis Miltoni, Angli, pro Populo Anglicano Defensio contra Claudi Salmasii Defensionem Regiam* ("John Milton, Englishman, in Defense of the People of England Against Salmasius' Defense of the King").

When John Phillips placed a freshly printed copy in his hands Milton fingered its pages silently. "I cannot read it," he said, at last. Only a dim haze of light was left of his eyesight. Mary, standing beside him, began to weep.

The job had been so well done that people commonly said the two things which had done most to raise the reputation of the Commonwealth in Europe were Milton's books and Cromwell's battles. It was considered that he had crushed Salmasius by a combination of insults and arguments. The pamphlet spread everywhere and its benefits were felt in practical problems of diplomacy.

Aside from the familiar case against the King, Milton had sketched a rare portrait of Salmasius as a doddering, effeminate, henpecked man; a dull, super-pedant in an age of pedantry, who wrote weakly in slipshod Latin. Not everyone was impressed by the arguments on either side. The famous Thomas Hobbes dismissed both of them. "Both are very good Latin, so that I know not which is best," he said, adding, "and both are very bad reasoning, so that I know not which is worst."

The council was delighted and passed a resolution "taking

note of the many good services performed by Mr. John Milton, their Secretary for Foreign Languages to this State of Commonwealth, particularly for his book in vindication of the Parliament and people of England against the calumnies and invectives of Salmasius." John was satisfied.

There was little peace for him. He had been dragged through a tedious series of public petitions by Mrs. Powell, who demanded money from him on a claim concerning her dead husband's estate. His enemies were delighted to have his name bandied and abused before the commissioners as a kind of monster and unnatural husband. His malicious mother-in-law did not hesitate to drag out the bygone troubles between her daughter and her daughter's husband. Her lawyers described Milton as "a harsh and choleric man and married to Mrs. Powell's daughter, who would be undone if any course were taken against him by Mrs. Powell, he having turned away his wife heretofore for a long absence upon some other occasion." John settled the matter as fairly as he could and put it behind him.

His lodgings at Whitehall had been uncertain for several months. In spite of his services to the state, many in Parliament had no love for him, especially the Presbyterians. They worked tirelessly to have him turned out of his chambers that they might be given over to some members of Parliament. The council held off his enemies for awhile, but in December of 1651 the family was compelled to uproot itself again and move to a new home.

This time it was a pleasant garden house in Petty France, about a half mile from Whitehall, facing on St. James Park. Neighboring to it was the estate of that same Lord Scudamore who had presented Milton to Grotius in Paris. The park was a pleasure to him, even in the gathering darkness of his eyes, for his friends led him on walks in its cool fragrance. It was a fenced park with driveways for coaches, bowling greens, archery ranges, and a bathing pond. There were fruit orchards whose scent-laden branches, in blossom time, were a joy to Milton though he could not see them.

Friendships were his comfort here. For eight years this house was to be a kind of goal for pilgrims of all sorts, from England, the Continent, and New England across the water. From there, from a tiny colony then called Providence Plantation, insignificant in size but huge in spirit, Roger Williams came and spent much time with Milton.

They had met before, in 1644, drawn together at once by the kinship of their ideas. Then Williams had come, seeking a charter for his Rhode Island Colony. He published a powerful book called *The Bloody Tenet of Persecution for Causes of Conscience*. The same thing was happening on both sides of the water. The Presbyterians in England, free of the bishops, were beginning to persecute the Puritans. The Puritans in Massachusetts, free of bishops and Presbyterians both, were persecuting everybody who disagreed with them. Roger Williams had been hounded out of Massachusetts by them. He founded the first Baptist church in the new world. Before long his Baptists, too, became so narrow that he cut his ties with them.

The Rhode Island settlement was planned as a pure democracy with absolute freedom of conscience and worship as its foundation. Even in his dealings with the Indians Williams was unusual. A little ditty by Arthur Guiterman says,

> The Pilgrims landed, worthy men,
>   And saved from wreck on raging seas,
> They fell upon their knees, and then
>   Upon the Aborigines.

Unlike them, Roger Williams bought his land from the Indians and lived more successfully among them than any other early settler.

His second trip to England was for two purposes, to get from the new government a broader charter, and to see for himself the great struggle for freedom in which he had so deep a stake. Many hours were spent at Petty France, for no one could give him so good an account of the state of affairs as his fellow Puritan, of like free spirit.

Besides politics and religion they spoke of languages and learning. Two great teachers exchanged teachings. Both men, wounded and betrayed by each established church they had supported, were moving to the belief that ministers of God were apt to be hindrances more than helps in true and free faith. Roger had just published a new work of his own, *The Hireling Ministry none of Christ's.* If men could have no passionate faiths without hating those who disagreed with them, where could freedom be looked for? A fool can ask questions that wise men cannot answer. These two men were wise, in their way, but could not answer it.

Roger quoted his friend, approvingly. " 'New Presbyter is but Old Priest writ large.' That is true, but you have seen it only so far. From New England I could add to that by changing it to New Puritan and Old Presbyter. They persecute lustily in Plymouth and Salem in the name of God."

Milton passed his hand wearily over his face. "You think it will follow here?" he asked.

"I think it will. Why shouldn't it? What is different in the natures of men? If this Parliament endures you will reap a Presbyterian tyranny."

"That cannot happen," John said angrily. "It would be intolerable. We did not take the head from Charles's shoulders for such an end. If the Presbyterians seek to maintain this Parliament and their bigoted ordinance of faith they will surely fail."

"And what will follow them?"

"I cannot see so far," John answered. "The weight of that may rest upon the shoulders of the Lord General Cromwell, whom I pity for it. He is the most tolerant and generous godly man in England."

"So you may think," said Roger, "but I am more skeptical than you, of one good man's power, when that power is force. Behind Cromwell are the Independents, whom he will no more be able to check than he now can check the Presbyterians."

"And so you say? . . ."

"And so I say, beware, think, before you follow even him."

"Look you, Roger, can we endure a Presbyterian persecution?"

"No, but what profit will you reap if you throw it off to fall under a fresh one?"

The fruits of restless nights of doubt and wondering were in John's mind. He would let Williams sample them.

"Perhaps there is an awful 'must' we face in this, Roger. You cannot surely prophesy a new tyranny but you can surely recognize a present one. To hesitate because we cannot see what will lie ahead would be as useless as to shrink from death because we only know by faith what may be in the after-world. We may believe or doubt but we must march into death, nevertheless."

"Yes, John, but there you have no choice. Here you have."

"Have we? If you love freedom and do not have it you have no choice but to seek it. Your own life has been built on that necessity."

"Yes, but I have not tried to do it with the sword. I have turned my back and withdrawn to where I could be free."

"You cannot always withdraw," John said, "although to do

so as you did is no cowardice but a great courage. But England as a whole is forever England and cannot withdraw from the thing that England is. When it is wrong it must change or be changed."

"Then do you see clearly what you will do?"

"No, no, I am not so fortunate. But I have a way of thought that grows upon me as I look back over the way that I have come. I had no quarrel with prelacy, except that it tyrannized the soul of man. I had no quarrel with Charles, or any king, except that he did likewise. I went against both for that cause. Now there is a Parliament and a church of Presbyterians that try to bind the freedom of worship. What can I do but go against them? It is possible that there may then be a government of Independents that will do as they have done in your New England. You have met it there by moving to another place. But if there were no unsettled place left in that great new world you would have to do as I must do here.

"It begins to mean this, to me, Roger. We must go against tyranny for the sake of liberty, always and forever. If it is objected that a risk is run that after the struggle there will follow a new tyranny then you answer, 'Yes, that risk must be run.' If it does not happen, all is well. If it does happen, then there is a new fight against tyranny. That way, whatever happens, the movement is forward, through tyranny after tyranny to liberty after liberty. But if we stop, we stand still with tyranny, or slip ever backward through old tyrannies returning so that they must all be fought over before the forward march begins again. I will not stay my hand because a man shall say to me that today's liberty will breed tomorrow's new tyranny. I say to him, tomorrow's tyranny, if that be true, will breed the next day's liberty again."

Williams was thoughtful for a long silence. "If you are right,

John," he said finally, "it is of that breed of argument which we can neither reject nor accept wholly. Whenever it shall prove to be, as it may be now, the argument of necessity, it will be right by the eternal rightness of necessity. I, for mine, thank God for my New England. I will not have to see the time there when a man can no longer withdraw himself from the quarrel."

Roger Williams went, soon, to his Rhode Island as president of the little colony. He would die in poverty and loneliness when the people of a world far behind him in its thoughts and ideals rose in a tide, flooding the dikes and engulfing his tiny, high-minded settlement.

For a time no great work fell to John's hand. He was too stricken by his eyes, and was led daily back and forth to the council hall. Oliver, and the other councilors, moved at his plight and grateful to him, were exceedingly anxious that he should continue his duties. They provided Milton with an assistant to carry out the routine tasks where his rare gifts were not required.

He used the influence of his post for kindly services more than once. Sir William Davenant, who had been poet laureate under Charles, was captured at sea through the ill-luck of being passenger upon a ship seized by the navy of the Commonwealth. Brought back to London, he was flung into the Tower, his life at stake.

Milton, who knew him slightly, was troubled and interceded with the council. "Sirs, Sir William is no enemy except through chance of birth and habit. He is a man of honor and ability, a kind of ornament to our learning. It would be wise and generous to spare him. I will answer for his honorable behavior."

The council granted the favor to their secretary. Davenant,

paroled as a prisoner at large, was grateful. "This is bread cast upon the waters, Mr. Milton," he said. "If it ever lies in my power I shall see that it returns."

The next entry in the big Bible was written by John Phillips' hand, for Milton was now totally blind.

My daughter Deborah was born the 2nd of May being Sunday somewhat before 3 of the clock in the morning 1652.

My wife her mother died about 3 days after. And my son about 6 weeks after his mother. 1652.

Total blackness three times over! The last glimmer faded from his eyes. The wife, whose simple, familiar companionship had become a fixed and important thing in his life was snatched away from him. He had sat, the two last days, constantly beside her bed. He could not see her as her life ebbed, still a girl and barely twenty-six, in the same fatal month that he had met her. Gently he had touched her face and hair, had felt the faint, failing breath from her lips. She was frightened, he knew, and he could not help her. In his blackness it seemed to him that he was living in that same death toward which she slipped so swiftly. Soon she was gone.

Then, in a scant six weeks, the sickly little boy slipped away from her. Hope of future was dashed. The companionship and comfort he had tendered to old John Milton would not be tendered to him by another John.

The load was greater than he could bear. What was a lonely blind man to do with three small daughters, one of them an infant? He engaged a new servant to keep the house and care for the children. There would be a succession of servants. How could he see that all was managed right, his children trained properly, his accounts honestly handled? John Phillips was his only companion. He could help, but he was a young, careless man, not skilled at such supervision.

Milton stumbled and bungled about the house in darkness. Even the familiar rooms were a danger to him. He fell heavily, more than once, and cut his head. Each piece of furniture, moved ever so slightly from its accustomed place, was a menace and a trap. In a blind man's house all things must be stationary and fixed. The little girls moved things and left them in his accustomed paths. He fretted and fumed at the helpless dependence upon guiding hands.

Often he took a book into his hands and stood helpless at the barrier that kept him from its use. If John Phillips were not at home Milton had to wait. He would scrawl some hasty note until his next dictation, or he would grope for the pen and could not find it, racking his mind to remember the lines he had thought of until his nephew should return. The long conditioning process had started. His mind must train itself to construct and preserve the webs of thought like a storehouse until the rare times when it could be emptied. He learned not to overcrowd it. If he tried to carry too much in his head he lost it all.

His thoughts had turned to Galileo. "Nothing is more useless than a blind astronomer," the aged man had said. Yes, but Galileo, heavy as the burden was, had been old and full of years. John, on the other hand, was in his prime, forty-four years old.

Oliver's task grew more thankless every day. The Rump Parliament, owing its existence to Pride's Purge, had been a sort of military rule. To Cromwell and the other army leaders it was a thing contrived in a crisis, intended for no long life. England must have proper representative government. The Rump must dissolve itself and a new Parliament be elected to succeed it.

But the Rump would not dissolve itself. "Now that the King is dead and his son defeated, I think it necessary to come to a settlement," Oliver said to Parliament after the campaigns of 1651.

It refused, and passed a measure undertaking to disband in three years. The tolerant army accepted the compromise but insisted that it begin to make the plans for calling the new Parliament that should then follow. The Rump proposed a measure which called for elections to fill up the vacant seats but which would continue the present members in their places without standing for re-election.

Oliver was enraged. While the Rump existed, he, with the army, was the true power in England. He did not want this power. It must be returned to the people. "As for the members of this Parliament," he said, "the army begins to take them in disgust. I would it did so with less reason. There is little to hope for from such men for a settlement of the nation."

Cromwell would not hear of making the present members permanent. His old friend and fellow council member, Sir Harry Vane, was urging the measure in the House. Oliver exacted the promise from him to hold the matter over for further debate.

The following day, whether by Vane's fault or not, the bill was introduced again and the House was about to pass it. In despair, Oliver hastened to the Commons, with a band of troops. He left his musketeers outside the door and took his place. To his neighbor, St. John, he whispered, "I am come to do what grieves me to the heart." Once more he faced decision without shrinking. "It is contrary to common honesty!" he burst forth, as the Parliament prepared to make itself permanent in power.

To Harrison, another member, he whispered, "The time has come."

"Sir," Harrison whispered back, "the work is very great and dangerous, therefore I desire you seriously to consider of it, before you engage yourself."

Speaker Lenthall rose to put the question to a vote. Appalled and outraged, Cromwell leapt up and began to speak. He denounced the shamefulness of the whole proceeding. "Your hour is come," he cried, "the Lord hath done with you!" There were cries of protest. Oliver slapped his hat upon his head in a gesture of contempt. "Come, come," he continued, "I will put an end to your prating! It is not fit that you should sit here any longer! You should give place to better men! You are no Parliament."

Sir Peter Wentworth cried out against such un-Parliamentary language. Oliver was not listening. "Call them in! Call them in!" he shouted. His musketeers entered and the members of the House, in fright and confusion, began to crowd toward the doors.

"This is against all right and all honor!" Vane shouted.

Cromwell spun around and answered bitterly. This man, in particular, he felt, had betrayed him. "Ah, Sir Harry Vane, Sir Harry Vane, you might have prevented all this, but you are a juggler, and have no common honesty! The Lord deliver me from Sir Harry Vane!" He turned about and pointed to the great mace on the Speaker's table. "What shall we do with this bauble?" he asked. "Take it away."

As the panic-stricken members flocked from the hall he cried out after them, "It is you that have forced me to this. I have sought the Lord night and day that He would rather slay me than put me upon the doing of this work."

The Lord had not heeded and the work now was done. The doors of Parliament were locked. What more had the old adversary, Charles, ever done?

The strange destinies of a nation have seldom had a more

able or a more unwilling tool than Cromwell. As leader of the army he had the only real authority. He wished to rid himself of it, yet first, order must be restored. There was such hatred and intolerance among all the differing religious and political groups that to drop the hand of discipline before some system had been agreed upon would have led to bloody anarchy. In despair he said, "Misrule is better than no rule, and an ill government, a bad government, is better than none!"

He sent out writs for a hand-picked Parliament of godly men, seeking honestly to draw from mixed opinions. The first hitch came when some refused to serve. Those who consented convened as a Parliament on July 4, 1653. This body had a brief life and became contemptuously known as "Barebones' Parliament" after Praise-God Barebones, a bigoted and eccentric leather seller of Fleet Street, who was one of its members. In a very short time this assembly handed to Oliver a so-called "instrument" of government and disbanded. They had been able to agree on nothing else.

Some urged Oliver to make himself king. "How else does a royal line have its beginnings but with a successful soldier?" they asked.

But Oliver did not want a crown and the army did not want a king. Yet he must assume some formal and more or less permanent leadership or proper government could never be restored. On the sixteenth of December, 1653, under the provisions of the "instrument," he accepted the title of Lord Protector of England, Scotland, and Ireland. Henceforth he signed himself not Cromwell, but simply Oliver P. ———— Oliver *Protector* had succeeded Charles *Rex*. Apparently it did not occur to Milton that new Protector is but old King writ large.

Chapter 11

"They Also Serve
Who Only Stand and Wait"

J OHN, under the hard choice he had mapped out to Roger
Williams, had gone wholeheartedly along with Oliver in
the creating of the protectorate. Oliver's honesty was unques-
tioned by him. Even in the grief and shock of Mary's death,
when no memorial was penned to her, he had addressed a sonnet "To the Lord General Cromwell." He praised him first,
calling him:

> Cromwell, our chief of men, who through a cloud
>   Not of war only, but detraction rude,
>   Guided by faith and matchless fortitude,
>   To peace and truth thy glorious way hast ploughed . . .

But it was not for praising that he stirred himself in his own
days of sadness, but to urge this leader whom he trusted to
the noblest aims of government and leadership.

> Yet much remains
> To conquer still; peace hath her victories
> No less renowned than war: new foes arise
> Threatening to bind our souls with secular chains:
>   Help us to save free conscience from the paw
>   Of hireling wolves, whose gospel is their maw.

With the ending of Council government, John might have
felt it was an appropriate moment to drop tasks that were
heavy, no matter what help was given him. But the Protector

had particularly asked him to continue to do what he could. Possibly something in the situation appealed to Milton's vision of an ancient ideal—the poet at the side of the ruler. Whether he saw himself so, or not, he stayed, continuing the flow to other nations, as Thomas Carlyle later wrote, of "what Oliver Cromwell meant and John Milton said."

Outside troubles were brewing for the Commonwealth. A naval war flared up with Holland. By all rights, the older republic of Holland, Protestant likewise, should have been friend and brother to the new republic in England. Fear of revolutionary changes and rivalry in sea power and merchant shipping choked this natural friendship. Holland had made herself the welcoming refuge of the exiled Stuarts.

Liberal minded men, such as the young William Penn, were troubled at this warfare. It fell to Milton to write the explanations and facts of the quarrel and plead the justice of the English cause. The triumph of the English fleet under the great Admiral Robert Blake was the first international success of the Commonwealth.

In 1652 the only important answer to his *Defense* against Salmasius had appeared. It was called *The Cry of the King's Blood to Heaven*. Although published in The Hague, it was the work of a secret Royalist, of French origin, named Peter du Moulin, who was living in London and often crossed Milton's path. Milton, at the time, firmly believed it to be the work of Alexander More, a Scotsman who was master of a Protestant school in Holland. More had written an introduction to the pamphlet and helped to prepare it for publication. It was natural to suspect him of writing it.

The council instructed John to answer him. He preferred to hold his fire. Salmasius was said to be preparing an answer of his own. But in 1653 Salmasius died. He had completed no answer and one opinion was that he had been so humiliated by

Milton's defeat of him that his death resulted from it. In any case, there was now no one to answer except the supposed author of *The Cry*.

The pamphlet had been sweeping in its abuse of Milton's character. It reported that he had been expelled from Cambridge for riotous living and that his trip on the Continent had been an escape from disgrace. It was the first to make the many-times repeated charge that his blindness was the punishment of God for his wickedness. Some were already saying that a drop of the King's blood had quenched his eyes.

John had asked for Andrew Marvell as his assistant. With his aid, and John Phillips', he lost no time preparing his *Second Defense*. There were at least three clear purposes in it. He began by a relentless mockery of More's personal sins. It happened that these were something of a minor scandal already. The poor man quailed under the wrath that fell upon him for a book he had not written. Peter du Moulin was vastly amused to see another man take so brutal a punishment that should rightly have been his.

In answer to the smears against his own character, Milton wrote a long, autobiographical sketch, relating all the main events of his life. He rose to heights of eloquence and pride until his pamphlet contained a song of self-praise which makes us feel, blinded and attacked though he was, that he was strengthening for himself the house of pride and purpose in which his spirit dwelt.

His faith in the ever-forward-moving fight for liberty was reaffirmed with all his power. He defended again the killing of the King, defended Pride's Purge, and the protectorate.

Yet this was not all. He gave a long account of Cromwell's career that began with praise but, as the sonnet had done, urged him on to his highest destiny, befitting his position as "leader of our councils, general of our armies, and the father of your country." He did not hesitate to point the way. "Do you then, sir, continue your course with the same unrivaled magnanimity; it sits well upon you; to you our country owes its liberties; nor can you sustain a character at once more momentous and more august than that of the author, the guardian, and the preserver of our liberties."

Confidently he suggests reforms and programs, boldly he criticizes possible tendencies away from liberty. So firm in viewpoint was the pamphlet that More, when answering it, attacked Milton in the King's name for the presumption of offering so much advice to the Commonwealth.

In 1655 his duties were lessened and his salary was reduced. At the same time he was awarded a modest life pension. Much good it would do him. Most of the work of his office was done now by other men. He was tired, handicapped, and troubled for the future of the Commonwealth. Now, in spite of his faithful public service, the strong bent of his thoughts was back toward the delayed career of poet.

Several fine sonnets came, not far apart. One of them, "On the Late Massacre in Piedmont," cried out against a ghastly massacre of Protestants in Italy at the foot of the Italian Alps. Cromwell was powerfully outraged. The English fleet sailed to the Mediterranean to intercede for the Piedmont Protestants and the power of the Protestant commonwealth was felt by all the Catholic monarchies of Europe, save only France.

Two sonnets loftily lamented his blindness and pledged the unshaken valor of his spirit. To his friend Cyriack Skinner he addressed one of them.

> Cyriack, this three years' day these eyes, though clear,
>   To outward view, of blemish or of spot,
>   Bereft of light their seeing have forgot,
>   Nor to their idle orbs doth sight appear
> Of sun, or moon, or star throughout the year,

Or man, or woman. Yet I argue not
  Against Heaven's hand or will, nor bate a jot
  Of heart or hope; but still bear up, and steer
Right onward. What supports me, dost thou ask?
  The conscience, friend, to have lost them overplied
  In liberty's defense, my noble task,
Of which all Europe talks from side to side.
  This thought might lead me through the world's vain mask
  Content, though blind, had I no better guide.

The other is less proud and strangely anticipates the foreboding sonnet of the young John Keats, with the breath of death upon him, who cried out, "When I have fears that I may cease to be, Before my pen has gleaned my teeming brain." For Milton it may mark the greatest doubt under which he ever suffered, of his ability to fulfill the high destiny he had always claimed.

When I consider how my light is spent
  Ere half my days, in this dark world and wide;
  And that one talent which is death to hide,
  Lodged with me useless, though my soul more bent
To serve therewith my Maker, and present
  My true account, lest he returning chide;
  Doth God exact day-labour, light denied,
  I fondly ask? But Patience, to prevent
That murmur, soon replies, God doth not need
  Either man's work or his own gifts; who best
  Bear his mild yoke, they serve him best: his state
Is kingly; thousands at his bidding speed,
  And post o'er land and ocean without rest;
  They also serve who only stand and wait.

Some time earlier his friend Leonard Philaras, a Greek, had written him from Paris. He was acquainted with a famous oculist who might yet be able to save John. He asked for details of the case. John wrote back at length.

"As you have, therefore, suggested to me that I should not give up all hope of recovering my sight, and told me that you have a friend and close companion in the Paris physician, Thevenot, especially distinguished as an oculist, and that you will consult him about my eyes if I furnish you with means for his diagnosis of the causes and symptoms, I will do what you advise, that I may not haply seem to refuse any chance of help offered me providentially.

"It is ten years, I think, more or less, since I felt my sight getting weak and dull. . . . In the morning, if I began, as usual, to read anything, I felt my eyes at once thoroughly pained and shrinking from the act of reading, but refreshed after moderate bodily exercise. If I looked at a lit candle, a kind of iris seemed to snatch it from me. Not very long after, a darkness coming over the left part of my left eye (for that eye became clouded some years before the other) removed from my vision all objects situated on that side. Objects in front also, if I chanced to close the right eye, seemed smaller. The other eye also failing perceptibly and gradually through a period of three years, I observed, some months before my sight was wholly gone, that objects I looked at without myself moving seemed all to swim, now to the right, now to the left. Inveterate mists now seem to have settled in my forehead and temples, which weigh me down and depress me with a kind of sleepy heaviness, especially from mealtime to evening; so that not seldom there comes into my mind the description of the Salmydessian seer, Phineas, in the *Argonautics*:

> All round him then there grew
> A purple thickness; and he thought the earth
> Whirling beneath his feet, and so he sank,
> Speechless at length, into a feeble sleep.

"But I should not forget to mention that, while yet a little sight remained, when first I lay down in bed, and turned myself to either side, there used to shine out a copious glittering light from my shut eyes; then that, as my sight grew less from day to day, colors proportionately duller would burst from them, as with a kind of force and audible shot from within; but that now, as if the sense of lucency were extinct, it is a mere blackness, or a blackness dashed, and as it were inwoven, with an ashy gray, that is wont to pour itself forth. Yet the darkness which is perpetually before me, by night as well as by day, seems always nearer to a whitish than to a blackish, and such that, when the eye rolls itself, there is admitted, as through a small chink, a certain little trifle of light.

"And so, whatever ray of hope also there may be for me from your famous physician, all the same, as in a case quite incurable, I prepare and compose myself accordingly; and my frequent thought is that, since many days of darkness, as the wise man warns us, are destined for everyone, my darkness hitherto, by the singular kindness of God, amid rest and studies, and the voices and greetings of friends, has been much easier to bear than that deathly one. But if, as is written, 'Man shall not live by bread alone, but by every word that proceedeth out of the mouth of God,' what should prevent one from resting likewise in the belief that his eyesight lies not in his eyes alone, but enough for all purposes in God's leading and providence? Verily, while only He looks out for me and provides for me, as He doth, leading me and leading me forth as with His hand through my whole life, I shall willingly, since it has seemed good to Him, have given my eyes their long holiday. And to you, dear Philaras, whatever may befall, I now bid farewell, with a mind not less brave and steadfast than if I were Lynceus himself for keenness of sight."

As John supposed, nothing was to come of this letter, but it was brave. The brave deserve the fair. Whether she was fair or not we do not know, and it was a matter of supreme indifference to a blind man, but Milton was now to turn again to the love of a woman.

She was Katherine Woodcock, of Aldermanbury, the daughter of a Captain Woodcock. As learned as Mildred Davis, she was gentler of nature and more steadfast of purpose. Her voice was soft and well modulated. She had the depth to love John Milton for what he truly was, not, as poor young Mary had, for a dream of a thing he was not. So it was no matter that he was older, although far from old. And it was no matter that he was blind. She loved the noble stamp that maturity and suffering had put upon his proud features. Even the armor of austerity that now, less than ever, could be set aside, held no terrors for her.

The thankless chore of running a blind man's house and rearing the children of another wife did not dismay her. To be, sometimes, the hand that wrote for genius was the next thing to genius itself if one were more than a mere hired scribe. And she could read to him with understanding, sharing what she read.

The marriage was a civil ceremony. Sir John Dethicke, a former Lord Mayor of London, joined their hands. It was November 12, 1656. So, if not light, there was warmth in Milton's home. His fears for the proper training of the girls were at rest. What better care could they have?

Anne was now ten years old, Mary eight, and Deborah was only four. He had neglected them without intending it. At times the clamor of their play was a burden to him as he strove to work, the more so now that he must study by fixing his mind with profound concentration upon the words of a reader often none too skillful.

The new household was happier for all of them. The tender

care of Katherine Milton was better for the girls than the slip-shod watchfulness of servants who knew their master could not spy upon their laziness.

John Phillips had left the household. Between himself and his uncle there was little truly in common. The gap had widened swiftly in the last year. Their roads were now to lie far apart. For all his upbringing in a Puritan house, the youth was now in a scrape with the censorship for having a hand in *Sportive Wit,* a book of bawdy poems. He was summoned before the council for his offense. Milton did not reproach him but the irrepressible young man, as though he had flung off suddenly the bonds of restraint, promptly issued another volume, *Wit and Drolleries.*

Edward Phillips had not stayed long at Oxford and had since been working for a London bookseller. He was more sober and akin to his uncle, and would now draw nearer as his brother left.

Oliver's protectorate was a dictatorship. The fact cannot be softened. It was a rule as absolute as Charles had claimed, and ironically, not being a monarchy, it lacked even the legitimacy of succession. What was to become of "The mountain-nymph, sweet Liberty" praised so early and so lately by Milton? It was government of the sword since the power, which Oliver was not anxious to have and had sought to avoid, was his by the will of the army. He knew very well, throughout his rule, that this type of power and government could neither last forever nor have the love of the people it governed. He found himself on a high spot with no way down from it; no way, that is, without the risk of chaos.

Under his guidance England's power and fame were at a peak. The force of Puritan arms was felt by the world on sea and land. There were intolerance and persecution through Pu-

ritan harshness at times, but Oliver, himself, remained tolerant
and sought to preserve tolerance. He could not always check
those who were his real power. Yet it was under his protectorate that citizenship in England was first granted to the Jewish
people. The land was opened for Jewry to enrich English culture as it has enriched the culture of all nations. The tradition
of Shylock was doomed and the road was opened for the people who, in a later day, would give to England one of her great
Prime Ministers, Benjamin Disraeli.

It is not easy to sum up Oliver's rule. He was hated by each
party which had sought to persecute its enemies when it had
the chance. Yet, while he held power, all were permitted to
exist. One of England's foremost historians, Lord Macaulay,
said, "Had it been a worse government, it might, perhaps, have
been overthrown in spite of all its strength. Had it been a
weaker government, it would certainly have been overthrown
in spite of all its merits. But it had moderation enough to ab-
stain from those oppressions which drive men mad; and it had
a force and energy which none but men driven mad by oppression would venture to encounter."

In the early summer of 1658 the Protector called Milton to
him at St. James's Palace, where King Charles had slept on the
last night before his execution. Had he been able to see, John
would have found Cromwell looking shrunken and ill, the
flesh loose on his large frame. There were lines of strain in his
face and a melancholy around his eyes. This thought was in
the Protector's mind.

"It is not the same man you would see, if you had the sight
you have sacrificed to this cause," he said.

"I have heard that you fail in body," Milton said, frankly,
"and am grieved for it. As for my eyes, in truth I have not
given them for you, for England, or even for my Muse. It has
simply pleased God to take them."

"I shall not add to your tasks, now," Oliver continued. "Nor shall I rule England long." He paused at length while the blind man sat patiently. "I had never designed to rule England, ever. Necessity hath no law." Milton remembered the phrase; Oliver had said it in a speech to Parliament some four years earlier. Clearly the fact haunted him. Did he think, now, of what he had added then: "Feigned necessities, imaginary necessities . . . are the greatest cozenage that men can put upon the Providence of God, and make pretences to break known rules by"?

The Protector changed his tone, as though to shake off a mood. "And, Mr. Milton, what of your Muse? Has she been abandoned wholly? What do you do for her—or she for you?"

"I have begun a work," Milton said. "It is of large scope and I shall have to pray for grace to finish it."

"What is its subject?"

The poet hesitated, reluctant to confess his ambition in work barely begun. "War in Heaven," he said.

Oliver mistook the hesitation that had preceded the answer, or chose to read into it his own thought, wryly. "A greater usurpation than is charged to me! The attempted dethroning of God Himself, rather than a king."

Milton was too absorbed for courtly protestations. He brushed past the Protector's ironic thought and added, "Its truer theme is Man's first disobedience and fall. Its attempt will be, with God's own help, to justify the ways of God to men."

The Protector saw all things as related to the drama in which he had been cast. "May God speed you with it," he said. "May you succeed in so mighty a task as well as you have succeeded in the petty one of justifying to men the ways that have brought me to this palace—this palace which I expect to leave before long by the only way open to me. It is only for that I called you, to give my thanks, once more. Whatever follows, and storms will follow, I hope they will not sweep you off and leave your work undone."

"I thank you," said Milton. "Though I have not been without such thoughts I could not have done, and would not do, otherwise."

Oliver stood. The blind man's sensitive ears interpreted the faint sound and he rose, too, less steadily. The Protector stepped forward, embraced him quickly and pressed his hand. Then he guided the poet across the unfamiliar terrain of the room to the door, beyond which Ned Phillips waited, to conduct him home.

In the ensuing weeks the sickness crept upon Oliver and on September third, he died. His last words were, "My design is to make what haste I can to be gone." England was tense with the fear of new civil war. It is some testimony to his government that his son, Richard, whom he had named as his successor, assumed the title of Protector without disturbance. Oliver was gone. God had freed England from the monster painted by the royalists. He had been offered a crown but had said, "I am ready to serve, not as a king, but as a constable, if you like!" So he had served as honestly and ably as he could; more so than some kings before and after him. He had cried out, in the trials of his office, "Indeed we are a crazy company, yet we live in His sight, and shall work the time appointed to us, and shall rest after that in peace."

The register of St. Margaret's Church, Westminster, where Herbert Palmer had called for the burning of the books of the divorcer, bears the record of a daughter born to John Milton and Katherine, October 19, 1657. Added to the date is the statement, "This is Milton, Oliver's secretary."

God had not yet tried his servant hard enough, as with Job. In February of 1658 Katherine died. Little Katherine, her daughter, died in six more weeks. It was six weeks after Mary that little John had died. Again the anguish of parting, this time from the truest love that he had known. Again the house without the care of a loving mistress; the girls once more motherless.

After one of the grief-tormented nights that followed, Milton raised the monument of a lovely sonnet to Katherine Woodcock. It is the testimony of his happy marriage.

> Methought I saw my late espouséd saint
>   Brought to me like Alcestis from the grave,
>   Whom Jove's great son to her glad husband gave,
>   Rescued from death by force, though pale and faint.
> Mine, as whom washed from spot of child-bed taint
>   Purification in the old law did save;
>   And such, as yet once more I trust to have
>   Full sight of her in Heaven without restraint,
> Came vested all in white, pure as her mind:
>   Her face was veiled, yet to my fancied sight
>   Love, sweetness, goodness, in her person shined
> So clear, as in no face with more delight.
>   But oh! as to embrace me she inclined,
> I waked, she fled, and day brought back my night.

It was the only time that he had ever seen her.

Chapter 12

"In Darkness, and with Dangers Compassed Round"

J OHN'S INSTINCT for politics was strong enough to make him feel that, with the death of Oliver, the Commonwealth was doomed. Cromwell had not done all things as Milton might have wished and had mainly disappointed him by failing to abolish the institution of an established church, yet John had trusted and followed him. The Protector's death grieved him greatly.

Andrew Marvell and he continued the divided duties of secretaryship for Richard, the new Protector. With him, and with the Parliament, Milton determined to press the matter to which he had not been able to sway Oliver. So, when the first Parliament assembled under the new protectorate, in 1659, he had ready another pamphlet called *Treatise of Civil Power in Ecclesiastical Causes showing that it is not lawful to compel in Matters of Religion*. With Oliver gone, no one else in power cared any longer for the matter of tolerance. The new plea for religious liberty was coldly snubbed.

Richard did not last long. He was an amiable and honorable man, gentler of spirit than his father. The strength and drive required to hold the reins of the protectorate were no part of his makeup. He could not deal with the Parliament nor with the chiefs of the Army, some of whom were jealous of him and anxious to sit in his seat. On the twenty-fifth of May, 1659, he abdicated with a sigh of relief. The rest of his life he would spend quietly on the Continent, glad to be rid of his too heavy destiny.

The old Rump Parliament had come together again. The government was now chiefly a struggle between it and the ambitious generals. Of these, John Lambert was the hungriest for power. George Monk, another of the stronger generals, cared less for power for himself but watched Lambert with a wary and suspicious eye.

While the Parliament was now, once more, the head of government, Milton sent them yet another argument: *Considerations Touching the Likeliest Means to Remove Hirelings Out of the Church.* Let them use the monies and properties of the established church of England to pay for liberal libraries and schools, leaving religion the informal, free matter that it should be. No one was interested.

In October, Milton's office was discontinued. He was again a private citizen. It was just as well, for with every passing week he found himself further at odds with the government.

Soon after Katherine's death he had begun the great epic which had been forming in his mind for years, in spite of the distractions of public life. It had been speeded by his blindness, for the new concentration that perpetual blackness brought to him turned his thoughts more and more upon poetic images and lofty fantasies.

The Fall of Man was to be his theme. *Paradise Lost,* he had named the poem. It would tell

> Of Man's first disobedience, and the fruit
> Of that forbidden tree, whose mortal taste
> Brought death into the world, and all our woe . . .

Through his mind raced thoughts so vast and lofty that the combined imaginations of his fellow writers in that day could not have grasped them. Certain of his closest friends, Andrew Marvell among them, for all their admiration, were appalled at the mighty theme he took and felt that he must surely break himself upon it and appear ridiculous.

"Things unattempted yet in prose or rhyme," Milton announced, and in the earliest lines formed in his mind and set down through dictation he called upon the fountainheads of inspiration to feed and nourish him to stand the test.

> What in me is dark
> Illumine, what is low raise and support;
> That to the height of this great argument
> I may assert eternal Providence,
> And justify the ways of God to men.

Here was a proud man who would explain the ways of Almighty God, who would presume to take the measure of God and Satan, the two great antagonists, and sift out the justice of their quarrel to mortal eyes.

The poem began to move swiftly. All the years of delay had bottled up the power of his poetic genius. Now it was packed in him under pressure. To his daughter Mary, who wrote but poorly, and to his hired or his volunteer amanuenses, he poured out the lines and felt his spirit lifted and buoyed on their mighty crest.

It seemed that he would never work without interruption. Now the new thing in the air was a widening clamor for the King's return. People wanted the Rump Parliament disbanded and a new, free Parliament elected. Such a body would be likely to summon home Charles II and put an end to the long turmoil and strife that now seemed hopeless.

Then General Lambert, commanding the army in London, took it into his head to be a second Oliver. Suddenly he turned the feeble Rump Parliament out of doors once more and seized the reins of government.

The people were sick of Parliaments with swords at their backs. But the stern-faced soldiers who garrisoned the House of Commons had a look of iron invincibility. They were veterans at the game of defeating superior numbers. Who could hope to challenge them?

The challenge came from General George Monk, in command of the army in Scotland. With the news of Lambert's coup he made ready to act. Here would be a match of equals; a wing of the Roundhead army itself. General Monk had no desire to be Protector of England and to wear Cromwell's mantle. He wanted only to save England from a series of upstart dictatorships. His secret thoughts were not far from those who thought the only hope lay in the King's return. People feared perpetual military rule and a succession of little tyrants. Better to have back a king who, through the habit of entire history, Englishmen were willing to recognize as real authority.

Milton was horrified at the idea. To bring back Charles II to succeed to his father's throne could only mean to reverse the march of history and undo all that had been accomplished. Englishmen must face the hard task before them and build a true republic. Tyranny, or many tyrannies, might lurk along the path, but it must be undertaken. They must not turn back! They must not! Was the ideal of liberty and freedom, "the noble and puissant Nation" he had seen "stirring itself like a strong man after sleep," to crumble down to a heap of ruins, ruled over by a dissipated, frivolous, low-minded offshoot of the contemptible Stuarts? Not so, if he could help it.

"Mary! Mary!" he called. "Quickly, girl! Paper and pen."

The startled young woman came swiftly from the kitchen. Her father had sat bolt upright in the straight-backed armchair for a good two hours, motionless. She did not expect this call, after the long dictation of the morning.

"Yes, Father?"

"Paper and pen, Mary."

She drew together the writing materials on the big, tapestry-covered table. Unwillingly she settled to the task. Milton rose and stepped cautiously forward, his hand upon his chair, feeling for the safe familiar direction.

"Is it the poem, Father?"

"No, it is a heavier matter. I know you do not like the task, child," he said, a little sadly. "I would gladly save it for someone else's hand, but it will not wait."

A frown gathered her brows. "I hope it is not Latin," she said crossly.

"No, Mary—English."

Milton began to pace in the small, safe area that he knew. The words came, but with more hesitation than marked the flow of his well thought out verses. These were restrained, weighed words, and in the thoughtful pauses between them could be heard the swift scratch of the young girl's pen.

It was the ripened fruit of many days of sad meditation that Milton now entrusted to paper through the frail, impatient, uncomprehending instrument of his daughter's hand. Two forms of vision went into this work—that of Milton's mind and that of Mary's eyes.

Little more than a start was made when a knock came at the outer door. Milton's voice stopped, and Mary's hand, racing the few words it lagged behind the speaker, halted too.

"Come in," he called.

The door opened. Cyriack Skinner and Dr. Paget entered, bringing with them a raw gust of the January night.

"Good evening, John," Cyriack cried, cheerfully. "It's the doctor and I. We break in on your work, I know, and a good thing, I warrant. You must not spend every day and half the nights of winter penned in a room with your endless dictation. Think of the girls, if not of yourself." He smiled broadly at Mary.

"Well, Cyriack—well, Nathan," said Milton wryly, "friends are a gentle plague! Warm yourselves at the fire." He turned to the hopeful girl. "Be off, child. I said it would not wait, but now it must."

The girl slipped hastily away. She would not risk the chance that his guests might leave and her father change his mind.

In Milton's house, his friends took upon themselves the little tasks that would have been impertinent with another. So Cyriack stirred the fire and threw some sticks upon it. The host retired to his chair and gravely faced his friends. "Find your seats, gentlemen."

Dr. Paget could no longer restrain himself from the subject which had brought him here. "Monk has crossed the border from Scotland with his army."

"Yes, Doctor, I know it."

"What will come of it, John?"

"Monk will come to London, I think, before much time passes."

"And then what?"

Milton smiled wearily. "Then I think I smell kings in the air."

"All the talk is of a free Parliament," said Cyriack. "Everyone clamors for it."

"A free Parliament," Milton said, "will call home Charles."

"Do you feel certain it is such a bad thing?" questioned the doctor earnestly. "After the long, hard rule of the army, are you sure it might not be a good course?"

"Good course!" The easy tone of conversation was gone. Milton's voice was harsh, his hands clamped down with force upon the chair arms. "This stubborn whim of returning to bondage! Then what will they say of us, and of the whole English nation, but compare us to the foolish builder who began to build a tower and was not able to finish it?"

"But we did not finish it," protested the doctor. "Everything has been in turmoil since Oliver died. Perhaps the King may restore law and order again."

The pale, fine features of the blind man reddened. "A folly!" he declared, pounding again for emphasis. "A folly to make ourselves adoring slaves of a single person for setting our house in order. It is doubtful that he could or would do it. It is certain we could do it better for ourselves."

"You still have faith in the commonwealth?" asked Cyriack, quietly.

Milton hesitated, his hands seeking one another, the tapering fingers set tip to tip. "Do not judge it now," he cautioned, "for we have not yet made it. Give it a little while; it is well worth the waiting. Yes, Cyriack, I have faith in the commonwealth, held by the wisest men of all ages to be the noblest, the manliest, the equallest, the justest form of government."

"Well, but in the meanwhile, if we must wait, grant them back their king. When we are ripe for a commonwealth we will have it."

"No! No king to come will forget the fate of Charles I. They will be sure to fortify and arm themselves sufficiently against any such attempt, hereafter, from the people. We will be forced to fight over again all that we have fought, and to spend over again all that we have spent. Yet we will never come so far as we have come now toward our freedom."

Dr. Paget twisted in his chair from sheer perplexity. "But John, so many are against us; so many!"

"They who seek nothing but their own just liberty, have always the right to win it, and to keep it, whenever they have power, be the voices never so numerous that oppose it."

Cyriack Skinner rose and stepped to Milton's side, placing his hand upon his friend's shoulder. "You have begun to convert us all over again and we do not need converting. The real state of affairs must be reckoned with. Monk will come, you say. And very likely on his heels will come a free Parliament. They will call back Charles. Then it will go hard for many, and especially for you. That is what brings us here."

"Come! No soft advice for hard times!"

"Yes, soft advice to turn away coming wrath. The people will not be taught, now, even by John Milton. We think the King will come and that little remains except to guess the time. Then not only your principles, but your very life will be in danger. Do not make it worse by speaking now."

Milton smiled through tight lips. "You counsel me against my nature, Cyriack, though you do it kindly. If they are determined to enslave us again then they may allow us a little time more to speak freely and take our leaves of liberty."

"Now, John Milton," Dr. Paget cried, accusingly, "you are already at work! Do not deny it. You are already shaping your thoughts toward some great folly. We knew it before we came here, from love of you. Do not do it! Your friends beg of you. A double vengeance will fall upon your already threatened head. A blind man cannot take swift flight from his enemies. Do not tempt the lightning!"

"He is right," urged Cyriack. "To resist now will help nothing. We need you for some other day."

Milton rose impulsively, the stamp of stubbornness in his face. The unthinking move carried him nearly into the fireplace. He half stumbled on the hearth.

Cyriack was beside him and seized him by the arm. "You are

already in the frying pan," he said, laughingly. "Stay out of the fire. This proves our argument."

"You may be right," said Milton, clinging to his friend, "but I shall say my say. You are right, Nathan, I am working. I shall state my faith and hopes. If we are about to lose, as you think we are, no one shall later say it was because we had no plan, no distinct form, no ready way to establish a free commonwealth."

Yes, surely kings were in the air. Day by day larger numbers of people clamored for a free Parliament and for the return of Charles. Day by day persons in high places swung secretly or openly toward the King's cause. But the blind champion of republicanism would not take the Restoration meekly. Others came to him to back up the warning of Cyriack and Dr. Paget. Heedless of all of them he drove fiercely at his goal. The poem was put aside. The lofty dream of heaven and hell would have to wait for the lofty dream of earth and England.

His daughters and his hired secretaries were hard put to keep pace with the surge of Milton's thoughts. He knew very well that this might be his last great bid for liberty. He blocked it out in plain, undecorated language, addressed more directly to the men of England than anything he had ever written before.

When the army from Scotland began to move, revolt broke out all over London. People refused to pay taxes. Riots and demonstrations filled the streets and market places. Plotting began in high offices. The fleet sailed up the Thames and threatened Lambert's army. Lambert tried to take his own force north to stop Monk. He found himself abandoned by his men and wound up as Monk's prisoner, in the Tower of London.

Hard and dangerous decisions now had to be made. Monk did not want to make them. As he approached the city, Milton was ready and published the new pamphlet, addressed in part to Monk: *The Ready and Easy Way to Establish a Free Commonwealth.*

The title was bold and arrogant, in Milton's strongest mood. *The Ready and Easy Way,* proclaimed the eyeless man who felt every seeing Englishman to be blinder than he. *The Ready and Easy Way,* brashly advanced in black and white while every man in every place of power tormented his brains for the answer to England's problems. It was a frank admission that no free commonwealth had been established. At the same time, the undertones of the argument recognized that it would not be done.

It was more courageous and more defiant because of this. It was the fight of a great fighter who knows he is beaten and will not surrender, who knows there may be a road of escape behind him but will not turn and take it. Milton might have trimmed his sails honorably to ride out the storm. Instead, he spat into the wind.

None of the other pamphlets had reached so wide an audience. The response was instant. Waves of abuse broke over his head. The council issued orders for its suppression and for the arrest of its publisher.

Monk ignored it and early in February, after a period of honest hesitation, declared himself in favor of a free Parliament. London went wild. Praise-God Barebones had suddenly appeared in public life again, determined to resist the King. He was raising a little band of Roundhead fanatics whose fury had alarmed even Monk. Now, with their hopes so close to fulfillment, the resentful people gathered in Fleet Street and cast stones through the windows of Barebones' house. Like the frogs in the fable, they would have a king, whether he would be an idle log or a devouring stork.

John Milton had business in Cheapside. The house in Bread Street was still his property and its affairs must be managed. Ned Phillips came, on request, to guide him there. With the streets in a state of nearly constant riot it was not safe for his daughters to conduct him.

Ned twitted his uncle on the pamphlet. "Now, Nunc, do you think it safe to venture into Cheapside for the sake of a little rent? The author of *The Ready and Easy Way* is not a popular man just now, you know."

Milton groped about the room for his stick. "If you fear for yourself, Ned, for your sake I will carry a cup and be just another blind man."

"Come, Uncle, you hit hard for a mere sparring match. Still, it's not all a joke. You know what they say of you?"

"What now?"

"They say when the new Parliament assembles you will be trundled off to Tyburn prison, but that John Milton is so contrary to all nature he will insist on being taken in a wheelbarrow and not a cart."

Anne Milton draped the cloak around her father's shoulders and fastened it at the neck. "Ned Phillips!" she chided. "Mind your tongue. I will not trust my father with you if you mean to be so flippant a flibbertigibbet when he is in danger."

"Tush, daughter, if Ned Phillips is to guide me through the Valley of the Shadow it is no more than the shadow of my poor eyes."

"They say," said Ned, as he led his uncle through the darkening streets of evening, "that every rump roast in every butcher's shop in London is sold today to celebrate the coming end of the great Rump, now that Monk has declared himself. There will be a rare roasting of meats if I judge rightly from the fires preparing on every side."

Ned Phillips was not wrong. It was Saturday, February 11,

1660, that found them later threading their slow way back toward Petty France. Samuel Pepys was in the crowd that jostled them and he entered the sights in his diary that night.

"In Cheapside there was a great many bonfires, and Bow bells and all the bells in all the churches as we went home were a-ringing. Hence we went homewards, its being about ten at night. But the common joy that was everywhere to be seen! The number of bonfires, there being fourteen between St. Dunstan's and Temple Bar, and at Strand Bridge I could at one time tell thirty-one fires. In King Street seven or eight; and all along, burning, and roasting, and drinking for rumps. There being rumps tied upon sticks and carried up and down. The butchers at the May Pole in the Strand rung a peal with their knives when they were going to sacrifice their rump. On Ludgate Hill there was one turning of the spit that had a rump tied upon it, and another basting of it. Indeed it was past imagination, both the greatness and the suddenness of it. At one end of the street you would think there was a whole lane of fire, and so hot that we were fain to keep on the further side."

So, his nostrils filled with the rich aroma of roasting meats and pungent swirls of smoke, his ears ringing with the boisterous merriment about him that he could not see, John Milton made his way through the neighborhood of his youth. The happy crowds that shoved about him never guessed that in their midst walked the man who most fiercely hated that kingship, the hope of which caused their joy.

It was a sad and heartsick man, yet still defiant, who went to his dark bed, perhaps while Samuel Pepys noted down in his diary what were to him and so many others the glad events of the night.

On March sixteenth, the Rump Parliament dissolved itself. This was a novelty after so many times being turned out of the House of Commons at the point of a sword. The new, free Parliament would soon assemble. Now, more than ever, the King was hoped for. But the way was not certain, there was grumbling among the soldiers. Most Royalist well-wishers trod softly when not among friends.

But there were little happenings to show that not all king followers walked warily. As the old Parliament announced its end, all the folk of London again flocked into their streets to talk of their joys and fears, their guesses and rumors.

A crowd was gathered in the Great Exchange, which had been called "Royal" before the Commonwealth. Here there was a tall statue of Charles I. The revolutionists had left it standing in the days of his overthrow, but on the base they had written, in gold, the words *Exit tyrranus, Regum ultimus, anno libertatis Angliae, anno Domini* 1648, *Januarie xxx*. ("The tyrant goes, the last of Kings, the year of English Liberty, the year of Our Lord 1648, January 30."

At five o'clock in the afternoon the streets were growing gloomy. People drew closer to the bonfires for the March wind was penetrating. Suddenly the scattered attention of the crowd was drawn together in the direction of one strange sight. A tall man had entered the Exchange. Over his shoulder was a ladder and in one hand was a bucket of paint. Unknown to any there, he gave no greetings but marched straight toward the statue of the dead king. A silence fell upon the spectators.

The stranger set his ladder firmly against the pedestal and mounted a few rungs. Deliberately he painted out the gold inscription, every trace of it. Still on his ladder, he turned his back upon his work and faced the mob. He raised his arm and those closest shrank back, to avoid the splatter of paint. "They shall be used no more!" he cried out fiercely, flinging the bucket and brush to the ground. "They shall be used no more, for they have had the honor to wipe out the writing of rebels!"

The bewildered crowd stayed silent for a moment, then burst into cheers. The painter paid no attention. He picked up his ladder and withdrew as mysteriously as he had come. The merchants and bystanders honored his deed with a huge fire which they kept flaming in the Exchange throughout the night.

The health of Charles II was openly drunk. His portrait began to appear in Royalist houses, which would have been a little while before a hanging offense. Pepys says, "All the discourse now-a-day is, that the King will come again; and for all I see, it is the wishes of all; and all do believe that it will be so."

If blind Milton could not go forth to battle then the battle came to him, and he sat in the midst of it. Marchmont Needham, a roistering old fellow fighter, came to Petty France with a hastily penned manuscript. He read it to Milton, stopping frequently to make the changes and additions suggested by the poet. These two had worked together often in the early days of the secretaryship. Milton aided gladly, for the fight was lonelier now than it had ever been.

When their work was finished, Chapman, the printer, proved game enough to publish it. *Plain English,* it was called. Needham was thought to be its author but the hand of Milton was not hard to recognize in it. It was suppressed at once. Chapman lay low and Needham fled the country. Milton remained in Petty France.

His enemies raged against him. To every attack worthy of the dignity Milton made reply, fearlessly signing his name. He listened as his friends read to him *No Blind Guides,* one of the harshest pamphlets against him. Its text was, "If the blind lead the blind, both shall fall into the ditch." It blackened him with lies and sneered again at his blindness as a vengeance of God. It described him as a devil in human form whom no Christian would dare even to pray for. Over and over, Milton hurled back upon his fellow citizens the Biblical warning: "Ye shall cry out in that day because of your king which ye shall have chosen and the Lord will not hear you in that day."

When the new Parliament was at last gathered together, the fleet put out to sea and stood off Dover, waiting for the news that it might proceed to Holland and fetch home the King it longed for. On board the flagship, as secretary to one of the high officials, was Samuel Pepys.

On May first, Parliament recalled Charles, making "the happiest May Day that hath been many a year to England." The word was brought to the fleet and Pepys wrote: "Great joy all yesterday at London, and at night more bonfires than ever, and ringing of bells, and drinking of the King's health upon their knees in the streets, which methinks is a little too much."

On May twenty-fifth, England's King stepped back upon the soil of his realm at Dover. He came ashore in a small boat with footmen, courtiers, and a lap dog. Cheering, color-splashed crowds hailed him. Mingled again with the sober dress of the commonwealth were the frips and fineries, frills and furbelows, laces and satins of the cavaliers. No Roundhead dreariness here!

Charles, flanked by fawning admirers and bootlickers, was a magnificent dandy. A large, curled wig framed his features and flowed across his shoulders. His weak face with its sleepy eyes, prominent nose, and flabby, dissipated mouth, was carefully composed for the occasion with an expression of reverence toward God and England and loving-kindness toward his wayward subjects.

The Mayor of Dover, inflated with the glory that had fallen upon him, scraped and bowed and presented His Majesty with a Bible. Charles took it solemnly and turned his eyes upon the ground. "It is the thing I love above all things in the world," he said.

The laughter of Milton would have been harsh and bitter to see this lavish show. It was a choice joke from the man ever afterward remembered as "The Merry Monarch." It was a fine comedy of devotion to follow fourteen years of Bible rule.

Charles's progress to London was a continual fair. On the way, with strange emotions and a little nervousness, he reviewed the remnants, now "loyal," of the army that had slain his father and held him so long from his throne. They were sullen faced. One felt, had a sudden, bold leader arisen, they would have swept this foppish, idling King before them.

By a happy coincidence it was on his birthday, May twentyninth, that Charles at last entered London. Parliament set aside the day for everlasting remembrance and celebration.

Well before this, on May seventh, Milton had yielded to his friends and family and sought refuge. It was not easy to shake him from his wish to stay on at the well-known house in Petty France, where the great of England and the continent had sought him out.

But there were pressing reasons for him to go. Charles had agreed to sign a pledge of general amnesty, pardoning everyone who had been in the revolution or the Roundhead government. But he had shrewdly left open a means for the settling of political quarrels among his recent enemies by excepting from pardon any persons whom Parliament itself might wish to punish.

Milton was a shining target. There were many who would happily have pulled a cart to take him to the gallows. He had defended the execution of Charles I; he had been an official of the government; he had been the last and bitterest foe of Charles II. This was more than enough to destroy him.

The three girls trembled for themselves and their father. They could not beg him to escape for their words carried no weight with him. Cyriack Skinner and Dr. Paget, Andrew Marvell and Lady Ranelagh, John and Ned Phillips all joined to convince him that he must not stay.

"Where can a blind man hide?" he protested. "I cannot leave the country. There is no place I can go where they will not find me if they wish it badly enough."

"Away from here. Anywhere away from here," they insisted. "If they find you at once it will be the end of you. If they are delayed we can find a way to save you. Time is what we need. You have friends enough but they must have a chance to act."

John Milton did not want to run. The timid fears of the girls annoyed him. "Where are the sons I should have had?" he cried out to himself. "Where is the light that has gone from my eyes so that I cannot fight but must have others bear me up?"

He called for Mary and made her set down a few lines which he would find a place for in the great poem, which had gone untouched for many weeks now.

> Though fallen on evil days,
> On evil days though fallen and evil tongues,
> In darkness and with dangers compassed round
> And solitude.

Finally he yielded. Then plans were to be made. The girls would be safe enough, once he was gone, but they must be provided for. He had two thousand pounds with the Commissioner of Excise but now he found he could not get it. The changing government had destroyed investments and frozen savings. The most he could get was a bond for four hundred pounds. He went to Cyriack Skinner and made over the bond to him, stamping it with his seal of the two-headed eagle. Cyriack gave him the money gladly. This much was settled.

Now, at midnight, Ned Phillips came. All was arranged and Milton awaited his nephew, clad in cloak and broad-brimmed

Puritan hat, armed with his stout cane. Anne and Mary and little Deborah clung fearfully to him and burst into sobs when his
young escort appeared. Soberly he embraced them, one by one,
and kissed them. A pang of sorrowful love went through his
heart for these girls who vexed him so. If, at times, he thought
them a cross to be borne, was he not a cross to them and a harsh
father? As best he could, he gave them comfort and made a
show of joking.

"No tears, daughters. I merely go awhile to play a little game
of blindman's buff with Charles."

The rich spring fragrance from St. James Park greeted him
as he left the house. He paused to fill his lungs with the well-
loved odors. Then they made their way through the gloom.

"Where are we now, Ned?"

"At Smithfield Cross, Uncle."

"Ah!" Milton stopped and prodded thoughtfully at the
ground with his stick. "England's kings!" he said bitterly.
"Charles II comes now. Here at Smithfield, some three hundred years ago, you will remember if I taught you well, Richard
II treacherously betrayed and murdered that plain champion of
the people, Wat Tyler. Here were burned the martyrs of faith,
Popish and Protestant alike, by kings and queens. England's
kings!"

Ned Phillips led the remaining way to the ancient and se-
cretive place known as Bartholomew Close. In its quaint, narrow cluster of buildings, in the house of a loyal friend, John
Milton waited, while the malicious and high-tempered Parliament began its quarrel over whom it would deliver to the ax.

Chapter 13

"This Man Cuts Us All Out"

"IT IS SAID that Milton's book against the King of England has been burned by the hangman, that Milton is a prisoner, and that he may well be hung." So, in a letter in 1660, wrote Dr. Gui Patin, a conservative French physician, who had watched with glee the downfall of the English rebels.

So he might well be hanged, indeed, and John knew it thoroughly. His friends worked feverishly to head off his enemies. Every political hack on the King's side, especially those whose toes had been trodden on by the force of Milton's pamphlets, clamored for his blood. The ballads and broadsides of the triumphant Royalists bandied his name about with every old lie and slander that had ever been used against him. The Parliament lost no time indicting him, along with John Goodwin, for his writings for the commonwealth. Then, by order of the King, his books were burned throughout England, particularly his first *Defense* and *Eikonoklastes,* his attack against the King's Book.

A long brawl began in Parliament over the drawing up of the promised Bill of Indemnity and Oblivion, which Charles had guaranteed to sign. Most members of the House were secure only under its pardon, but they were no less eager to tack the names of their special foes to the specific list of those who were to be left out of the general pardon and punished. Over and over again the list was revised.

John had two friends who labored hard for him. The Royalist poet, Sir William Davenant, had not forgotten that Milton had saved his life when the fortunes were reversed. He had strong influence and used it generously. Andrew Marvell was staunchly loyal to his friend. He was now a member of the House of Commons for the city of Hull. To have Milton forgotten or forgiven was quite impossible. Their strategy must be to delay and hold back the vengeance of his enemies.

The blind man could not hide forever. Some intended victims had escaped from England. Such flight, the only kind that would save him, was impossible for John. His friends decided that a bold course, now, would be the safest. Let him give himself up, while the dispute was raging in the House, and while the wrath was directed, for the moment, away from him personally and to the burning of his books.

Andrew hurried to Bartholomew Close. Milton was nervous and fretful of the long suspense, ready to do anything.

"John, we have a place for you."

"And where is that?"

"In prison. It is there that they are least likely to think of you and work themselves up to a fiercer vengeance."

John was amused. "It is daring strategy. Do you think, then, that I should step into my fetters willingly? What if your guess is wrong, and, having me, they promptly clap a rope around my neck or hold me until I rot?"

"No, that will not happen. I will answer for it. And Davenant, who proves an honest, grateful man for all he is a cavalier, is working through the King for your pardon. It is the small men in the House who are your danger. Those who were timid when you were bold are the ones now bold when you are helpless. Safely pardoned, they want to punish others. It proves their new loyalty to our noble King! We can hoax them by a seeming imprisonment and then ask mercy for you."

Milton scowled. "It sits ill with me to be a seeker of mercy to a profligate King."

The practical Marvell dismissed him impatiently. "Come, that is only idle pride. To finish your poem is the thing that counts. This puny, worthless Charles is not worth spending your pride against. Let him sport with his mistresses and playmates. Meanwhile, we will get you free in whatever way we can and you will do a work that matters."

"Very well, Andrew, you are a wise man. You have an eye for first things first."

There was an old warrant out for Milton's arrest. Under its authority Andrew quietly delivered up his friend to a sergeant-at-arms of the House of Commons. He was placed in a comfortable room in the Tower.

Charles II was a lazy, pleasure-loving man with no energy for grave matters. If he was not fiercely vengeful it was not due to virtue but merely indifference. When Davenant, of whom he was fond, insisted on discussing with him the case of one John Milton, whose pamphlets the King well knew, he was both amused and bored.

"Come, Sir William," he said, "why so much fuming over a blind pamphleteer? I want the gentlemen of Parliament to be happy. If they want to hang him, then let them."

"Your Majesty," Davenant replied, "I am much in his debt. Moreover, he is no common pamphleteer but one of the first poets of your kingdom. I would have you let him return to his verse, which I assure you he will do quietly if released. He is now in prison. Allow me to use your weight to protect him from the shortsighted hatred of the House. It will do your name no good in future times to make a martyr of one blind poet."

"Take your poet, take your poet!" Charles said impatiently. "I ask only that I need not read his verses."

There were angry men in Parliament. Why was Milton's name still not on the list? If his books were burned he should burn with them. As Bishop Burnet said, "It was a strange omission if he was forgot and an odd strain of clemency if it was intended he should be forgotten." But the outcry was quieted. Davenant had used the King's clemency where it would do the most good. When the Bill of Indemnity was finally signed Milton's name was neither on the list of those condemned to die nor of those condemned to be punished short of death. Yet he was still in the Tower and still under an indictment so that the act of general pardon did not actually protect him.

When they judged the time was ripe, Marvell and other sympathizers in the Commons obtained a bill for John's release, magnifying the imprisonment to seem a punishment it had not been.

Milton was required to pay to the sergeant-at-arms a fee, or bill of costs. It seemed high to him and with supreme indifference to the delicate tact needed for the situation, he protested. He was ordered to appear before the House, with the sergeant, to state the case. This might be fatal. Marvell nipped it in the bud and ordered Milton to stay strictly at home. The matter came up in the House without his presence. A few members cried out angrily. What! The defender of the regicides, who should have been hanged, complaining about jail fees. Well, there was yet time to hang him! Andrew hushed the matter and the case was closed. John Milton was back in private life, a free man.

From the blue laws of the Puritan government England swung back to the farthest extremes. There was no more debauched, licentious court in English history than that of the Merry Monarch. Moral standards were tossed overboard by all except the small numbers of the steadfast in faith. The theaters reopened with bawdy plays performed by loose-moraled actresses, the mistresses of the King and his courtiers. It was an idle, frivoling time.

The bishops were back firmly in their power. No time was

lost in purging Presbyterians and Independents, together once again in persecution. There was another wave of migrations to New England. Harsh laws were passed requiring conformity to the worship of the Church of England on pain of death. A licensing system for books was set up, far stricter than that against which *Areopagitica* had been written. As late as 1664, a printer who dared to print excerpts from *The Tenure of Kings and Magistrates* was hanged, drawn, and quartered.

Dr. Gauden, the former Presbyterian who had written the *Eikon Basilike,* was maneuvering for the title of bishop in the Episcopal fold. No other single work had done such good for the cause of the King. He was rewarded, but not without a rebuke from Chancellor Hyde, against the parading of his boast of authorship of the King's Book. "The particular you mention has indeed been mentioned to me as a secret; I am sorry I ever knew it; and when it ceases to be a secret it will please none but Mr. Milton."

Worst of all was the continued fury against the late Commonwealth. By act of Parliament, on January 30, 1661, the anniversary of Charles's execution, the grave-snatched bodies of Oliver Cromwell, Henry Ireton his son-in-law, John Bradshaw, and Thomas Pride were hanged in their shrouds at Tyburn prison, until sundown. The heads were then cut off and their bodies were buried beneath the gallows. Even the grave of the Protector's mother was ransacked, and that of Blake, who had made England glorious upon the sea.

This was the treatment Englishmen found proper for the man whom Macaulay called "the greatest prince that has ever ruled England," extravagant praise that overlooks a number of kings and the greatest "Prince," as she always referred to herself, of all, Elizabeth I. Many good people must have been, like Mr. Pepys, ashamed and uncomfortable. Although his wife had been among the huge throngs of spectators who made the day a holiday Pepys had said, when Parliament declared its intention, "it do trouble me that a man of so great courage as he was should have that dishonor, though otherwise he might deserve it enough."

Time and its passing, so vital in political activities, now ceased to matter in Milton's life. The bitterness of defeat and the hopelessness of renewed fight, even as he had prophesied in *The Ready and Easy Way,* caused him to turn away from all forms of public life. He was exploring patiently into the far deeps of his own spirit.

The house in Petty France had been left. He was back in High Holborn, where he had once lived before. And soon again he moved, to settle in Jewin Street, near his old Aldersgate house. It mattered little where he lived, for his true life was wholly inward. He was devoted utterly to the massive fabric of *Paradise Lost.*

Here was the epic structure he had groped for all his life long. It had been clear and compelling in his mind since 1658, a little more than two years before. In spite of the tumult and chaos of those hectic years of collapsing government he had made some headway. Now it must be painfully and laboriously finished.

Patience, patience, patience was required; a tremendous, hellish, racking discipline for a high-tempered man. He must piece together blocks of the poem, twenty or thirty lines perhaps, in his mind and get them firmly set. Then he must wait his chance to dictate to his paid amanuenses or, if he could not wait, call Mary, for whom he often had to spell almost as many words as he dictated. Then he must hear this haltingly read back to him again and smooth it over, bettering his lines, adding or deleting, carrying in his head the overall flow and pattern into which each part must fit.

Milton was not easy to live with—indeed had never been so. Now the difficulties of his blindness, his disappointment in his hopes for England, the concentration of his great work, were enough, coupled with the natural heaviness of his nature, to make him harsh and irritable. He was beginning, now, to suffer from the gout, which caused his joints to swell and ache with arthritis.

He had endless troubles with the girls and they with him. It was a pity he had ever had them. They were born of a marriage that had been, at best, a compromise. Perhaps if Katherine had lived he would have learned to know them. But the frustration of her loss had made him worse. He had neglected the girls in spite of good intentions, knowing little of their needs or proper training, finding it hard to care. They were only wrangling voices in the dark. They were a burden to him.

The man so forward looking in his thoughts on education was so strangely warped in his view of women that he did not set store by education for them while, at the same time, he blamed them for their lack of education and admired learned women.

The oldest daughter, Anne, had been excused because her speech was halting. But Mary and the small Deborah were taught to read to him in Latin, Hebrew, and Italian without knowing so much as a word of what they read, as there are singers who learn only to pronounce a language, not to speak or understand it. They were put to this chore and hated it, and who can blame them? Yet, thought Milton, these girls were unimportant. There was a great work that he must do. So, if they were in his charge, he must make use of them what way he could. Anne could not write at all, Mary and Deborah but very poorly.

They resented the tasks their father set upon them. Sometimes, if they had led him out into the center of the city, they would run off after some interest of their own and leave him stranded in the crowded streets, forced to humiliate himself and beg the aid of strangers to guide him home, often meeting with jibes from those who had been Royalists and hated his name. He would get back, at last, to Jewin Street, exhausted and weeping with rage and shame, perhaps with some new block of noble verses lost and obliterated in his harried mind.

They conspired with his servant to cheat him in the marketing and household accounts, dividing the spoils with her, and using the petty sums for idle pleasures. They sometimes stole his books and sold them, robbing him of treasures that he could not duplicate.

Only a wife in the home could solve the problem. He did not hesitate when his old friend and physician, Nathan Paget, arranged a marriage for him with Elizabeth Minshull. She was a good soul, in her thirties, plain and quite unmatched with him in any way. For her it was a respectable marriage and security. For Milton, in his fifty-fifth year, it was necessity.

"They say your father will marry again," the maid servant said to Mary in the kitchen, when the thing was in the air.

"That's no news, to hear of his wedding," said Mary, sullenly. "Now if I might hear of his death, that would be something!"

The marriage was performed in February of 1663, by the Reverend Thomas Tomkyns. No civil ceremony this time, but by the book and letter of the Church of England as required by law.

The household, with its new mistress, moved now to the Artillery Walk, Bunhill Fields. Things were better. Betty Minshull had a touch of shrew in her but Milton humored her. He was happier with order in the house. For the girls it meant a discipline they did not always relish but which was sorely needed for their own welfare. The marriage was successful.

The poem was drawing to a close, though the work of revising and correcting it would consume another several years. He did not compromise himself. An offer was brought to him to enter the employment of the King. John was no turncoat. He would not write for the crown he had opposed. He was sought out by a nobleman as an authority on divorce. Admiring pilgrims found their way to him.

The Church of England could not defeat him, either. In 1664 he was arrested and fined for refusing to attend services. In the house of the Puritan, whose whole life, now, was a meditation on the ways of God, there was no religious observance whatsoever. The corruption of the times had soiled for him all common forms of worship.

He was remembered by many. John Evelyn employed Ned Phillips to tutor his son and jotted in his diary, "Mr. Edward Phillips came to be my son's preceptor: this gentleman was nephew to Milton, who wrote against Salmasius' *Defensio*; but was not at all infected with his principles, though brought up by him."

The great plague of London, in 1665, drove the Miltons into refuge in a cottage at Chalfont St. Giles, Buckinghamshire. The Black Death raged through the city sweeping all before it. Always present, never for centuries had it gained such headway. Religious fanatics considered it the smiting of the wicked like the plagues of Egypt. Seventy thousand died of it in the city of London. The streets were filled with processions of the dead.

Another disaster followed in 1666, less than a year after the plague. The Great Fire of London in four days destroyed four fifths of the city, almost all of it within the enclosure of the old walls. Milton's property on Bread Street was gone; St. Paul's, Whitehall, all the landmarks and fine buildings went. It was a new city, and a more roomy, healthful one, that grew slowly upon its ruins.

The epic was accomplished—no longer a dreamer's vision but a firm reality, a triumph. It had not been easy to find a publisher. Printers had good cause to shy off from this determined blind man. He was a suspicious character, the author of a list of forbidden books, thought of by hardly anyone as a poet. The ponderous work that he submitted to them was fantastically unlike the light love lyrics and swift, bawdy lines that were the style in poetry. He seemed prehistoric, a dinosaur of letters.

With some doubts, Samuel Simmons risked the publication, but not under his own imprint, not for the first edition. He was playing safe. It would be an honor to lend the name of Simmons to the second printing but how could a simple man foresee it? By an odd twist it was passed for its license by no other censor than the young Reverend Thomas Tomkyns, who had performed the wedding service for John and his third wife. He found nothing dangerous in it, which argues a certain dullness in his mind.

So, in the fall of 1667, appeared *Paradise Lost: A Poem written in Ten Books;* by John Milton. In later editions he rearranged it into twelve books, as it is familiar now. In his highest hopes he could not have foreseen its effects. In the next eighteen months it sold thirteen hundred copies. This, for the times, was a sort of bestsellerdom. The sheer force of genius had overcome resistance. The fallen and forgotten secretary to Oliver was suddenly a famous man again, reborn in a new role to the public eye. The shadow of disgrace was gone from him. He was respectable.

There were divided opinions. Some found the poem a monstrosity. Some were confused and puzzled by it, removed by such a gap of time, mind, and spirit from the noble Elizabeth-

ans that their tongues could only stumble on blank verse. This
was an era when the actor-author Colley Cibber, and even so
talented a poet as John Dryden, rewrote the plays of the actor-
author Shakespeare into jingling rhyme.

One of the light, amateur poets of the Restoration is said to
have written: "The blind schoolmaster, John Milton, hath published a tedious poem on the Fall of Man. If its length be not
considered its merit, it has no other."

Yes, there were tedious passages in it, but no vast work is
without them. In the next century, the great critic, Dr. Samuel Johnson, who disliked heartily both Milton's politics and
theology, said of *Paradise Lost,* "None ever wished it longer
than it is"—which is true. But he also said: "His great works
were performed under discountenance, and in blindness, but
difficulties vanished at his touch; he was born for whatever is
arduous; and his work is not the greatest of heroic poems, only
because it is not the first." That is, only because such as Homer,
Virgil, and Dante had written before him on the epic scale.

The fashionable literary arbiter in Milton's day was the
many-sided skillful-handed John Dryden. He was the prophet
of rhyming verse both in poetry and drama. He was able and
honest enough to know what was good and what was bad. For
all the liberties he took in adapting Shakespeare to suit a shal-
lower taste he was well aware that his generation was infer-
ior to the Elizabethans. With a backward glance at them he had
confessed:

> Our builders were with want of genius curst,
> The second temple was not like the first.

He received *Paradise Lost* in a way that did him honor. "This
man cuts us all out, and the ancients too," he said.

What was this fruit of Milton's inward vision; this light from his darkness?

It opens by invoking a source of inspiration that is the classical Muse of Greece blended with the creation-inspiring Holy Spirit of Christian faith, the Third Person of the Trinity. He asserts his ambition to tell

> Of man's first disobedience, and the fruit
> Of that forbidden tree, whose mortal taste
> Brought death into the world, and all our woe,
> With loss of Eden, till one greater Man
> Restore us, and regain the blissful seat. . . .

He begs the "Heavenly Muse" to aid his "adventurous song"

> . . . while it pursues
> Things unattempted yet in prose or rhyme.

> what in me is dark,
> Illumine; what is low, raise and support;
> That to the height of this great argument
> I may assert Eternal Providence,
> And justify the ways of God to men.

The story opens with the scene of a fiery lake in Hell, in which lie, stunned and shocked, Satan, and a legion of rebellious Angels who, with their leader, have been hurled there from high Heaven by the wrath of God. ("Satan" means "the Adversary," otherwise known as the Archangel Lucifer.) Lucifer and his followers had yielded to the primary sin of Pride, and had used their angelic powers to make war in Heaven against their Creator, seeking to overthrow Him and seize His Throne.

> A dungeon horrible on all sides round
> As one great furnace flamed.

Even in this moment of catastrophe the still defiant Satan, in his fury, dreams of new war and revenge.

> What though the field be lost?
> All is not lost.

He summons his strength to leave the lake of fire.

> Forthwith upright he rears, from off the pool,
> His mighty nature: on each hand the flames,
> Driven backward, slope their pointing spires
> . . . .
> Then with expanded wings he steers his flight
>   . . . till on dry land
> He lights.

They must make the most of the dreadful place where they find themselves.

> The mind is its own place, and in itself
> Can make a Heaven of Hell, a Hell of Heaven.
> What matter, where, if I be still the same,
>   . . . in my choice
> To reign is worth ambition, though in Hell:
> Better to reign in Hell than serve in Heaven.

To this end he will marshall his disordered army and set up a dark, evil kingdom of his own. To his prostrate followers,

> He called so loud, that all the hollow deep
> Of Hell resounded. . . .

issuing the challenge to take up once more the fight, and assert their strength and courage.

> Awake, arise, or be forever fallen!

They spring up in answer to his summons, responding to his purpose to attempt further mischief.

> . . . out-flew
> Millions of flaming swords, drawn from the thighs
> Of mighty Cherubim; the sudden blaze
> Far round illumined Hell. Highly they raged
> Against the Highest, and fierce, with graspèd arms,
> Clashed on their sounding shields the din of war.

There are tasks to be done. With mighty labors they speedily erect the huge palace of Pandemonium, Hell's capitol; the word means the place of all demons, or devils, and hence has come into common use to describe any scene of wild disorder and noise. Now, in their Hellish House of Parliament, they combine their wits to map some vast revenge.

In this Parliament of evil spirits some urge open warfare, the invasion of Heaven once again. Others, recalling the defeat they have suffered so lately, are for building and maintaining their own kingdom in Hell. Satan, supported by his chief lieutenant, Beelzebub, proposes a scheme that brings the whole assembly into agreement.

> There is a place
> (If ancient and prophetic fame in Heaven
> Err not), another World, the happy seat
> Of some new race called Man, about this time
> To be created like to us, though less
> In power and excellence, but favoured more
> Of him who rules above. . . .
>
> . . . .
>
> Thither let us bend all our thoughts, to learn
> What creatures there inhabit, of what mould
> Or substance, how endued, and what their power,
> And where their weakness, how attempted best,
> By force or subtlety. . . .
>
> . . . Here perhaps
> Some advantageous act may be achieved

By sudden onset: either with Hell fire
To waste his whole creation, or possess
All as our own, and drive, as we were driven,
The puny habitants; or, if not drive,
Seduce them to our party, that their God
May prove their foe, and with repenting hand
Abolish his own works. This would surpass
Common revenge, and interrupt his joy
In our confusion, and our joy upraise
In his disturbance; when his darling sons,
Hurled headlong to partake with us, shall curse
Their frail original, and faded bliss,
Faded so soon.

All consent. But the task of reconnaisance is hard and perilous. Who shall discover the whereabouts of Man and explore
the path? Satan himself is the volunteer. He alone has the
courage and cunning. In tribute to their king they stand.

Their rising all at once was as the sound
Of thunder heard remote.

At once Satan sets forth and makes his way to the gates of
Hell. These he finds guarded by Sin and her hideous son,
Death. Seeing Satan approach, Death rushes at him with lev-
eled spear, but Satan stands his ground and challenges him.

Whence and what art thou, execrable shape,
That darest, though grim and terrible, advance
Thy miscreated front athwart my way
To yonder gates? Through them I mean to pass,
That be assured, without leave asked of thee.

He explains his errand to the horrid pair and promises that
when he has corrupted Man, as he intends to do, Sin and Death
will have free range of Earth to glut their appetites unceasingly.

So, with her massive key, Sin turns the lock. The huge gates of Hell swing open.

Now the story elaborates upon the familiar one told briefly in the first three chapters of *Genesis*. Adam, whose name means "man," and the companion God created for him, Eve, whose name means "life," as signifying the mother, are living in tranquil joy in the Paradise of Eden.

In Heaven, God, seated upon His throne, sees the progress and purpose of Satan. He permits the fallen Angel to make his attempt because it is in accord with God's intention of creating Man as a free, rational, moral being that he should choose for himself whether to obey or disobey God. There is only one thing forbidden to Adam and Eve—to eat of the fruit of the Tree of Knowledge. Satan learns of this by eavesdropping on Adam and Eve's conversation and determines to prompt them to this act of disobedience, for which the promised penalty is death.

God not only foresees the attempt, but predicts to His Son that Man will yield to the temptation. This is a difficult theological point. People have asked: Why did God permit evil? And the answer is, that without the possibility of evil there is no possibility of good. Without the possibility of disobedience there is no possibility of obedience. There can be no free being, unless that being has the option of choosing the wrong course as freely as the right one.

God's anticipation of what Man would do did not cause or compel Man to do it. An observer hovering in a helicopter above the crest of a hill may foresee an inevitable collision on the road below as the result of one car trying to pass another while unable to see what is coming from the opposite direction. The man overhead can see the crash coming before any of the cars know about it—but his seeing it is not the cause of it. Prophecy is not compulsion.

As Milton unfolds the story, even before the temptation and fall of Man, God predicts it and the Son of God, Messiah, offers Himself in advance of the event as an eventual sacrifice for Man's Redemption. Thus we see that although God's free creature might disappoint Him, disobey Him, and stray from the right way, nevertheless God will not abandon Man, or leave him without hope. A way to atonement (at-one-ment), or reunion, will be provided through the free act of God's Son, but again, the free creature Man must decide whether or not to accept the offered redemption. Those who choose to do so may come to God; those who choose the converse way will be cast out with Satan to their just punishment.

The story advances. The Angel Raphael comes and warns Adam of the enemy approaching, explaining who he is and relating the history of the war in Heaven. Then, on a certain morning, Eve desires to wander alone, though she in turn has been warned by Adam. Satan approaches her, having entered the body of the Serpent, to control and speak through it. The Serpent does not yet crawl, but moves reared upright, a creature of strange beauty, with "turret crest and sleek enamelled neck."

He flatters Eve, calling her "Empress of this fair World. . . . Sovran of creatures, universal Dame!" She is astonished that he can speak, and asks how this has come to pass. It is because he has eaten the fruit of a certain tree that he has gained speech and reason, he explains. Eve asks to be shown the tree. When the Serpent leads her to the Tree of Knowledge, she exclaims that she is forbidden to eat of it, that God has warned:

> " 'Ye shall not eat
> Thereof, nor shall ye touch it, lest ye die.' "

The Serpent scoffs at her fears:

> ". . . look on me,
> Me who have touched and tasted, yet both live,
> And life more perfect have attained than Fate
> Meant me, by venturing higher than my lot.
> Shall that be shut to Man which to the Beast
> Is open?"

He comes, then, to the heart of the temptation, that sin by which he himself had fallen, Pride, the desire to be like God.

> ". . . ye shall be as Gods,
> Knowing both good and evil, as they know.
> That ye should be as Gods, since I as Man,
> Internal Man, is but proportion meet—
> I, of brute, human; ye, of human, Gods.
> So ye shall die perhaps, by putting off
> Human, to put on Gods—death to be wished,
> Though threatened, which no worse than this can bring!
> And what are Gods, that Man may not become
> As they, participating god-like food?"

No match for the Adversary's persuasiveness, Eve yields.

> . . . her rash hand in evil hour
> Forth reaching to the fruit, she plucked, she eat.
> Earth felt the wound, and Nature from her seat,
> Sighing through all her works, gave signs of woe
> That all was lost. Back to the thicket slunk
> The guilty Serpent, and well might, for Eve,
> Intent now only on her taste, naught else
> Regarded; such delight till then, as seemed,
> In fruit she never tasted, whether true,
> Or fancied so through expectation high
> Of knowledge; nor was Godhead from her thought.
> Greedily she ingorged without restraint,
> And knew not eating death.

Adam, coming to meet her, is appalled at what she has done. Partly persuaded by the arguments she repeats to him, and partly impelled by love to share whatever fate must be hers, Adam also eats of the fruit.

> Earth trembled from her entrails, as again
> In pangs, and Nature gave a second groan;
> Sky loured, and, muttering thunder, some sad drops
> Wept at completing of the mortal sin
> Original. . . .

Now their innocence is gone. Having chosen evil they are aware of evil as never before. They perceive that they are naked. That original nakedness was the symbol of their innocence; the new impulse to conceal bodies which are natural and good is the sign of a new kind of self-consciousness, the awareness that their unwillingness to be obediently content with abundant gifts, and to await patiently what more God might later grant them, has partly tainted, or corrupted, all good things for them. We see the change in their natures at once, subtly but unmistakably, in a tendency to quarrel and to blame each other for their mutual wrongdoing.

Before each book of the poem, Milton places an "Argument" or synopsis. After the fall, in Book Ten, "God . . . sends his Son to judge the transgressors; who descends, and gives sentence accordingly; then, in pity, clothes them both, and reascends. Sin and Death, sitting till then at the gates of Hell, by wondrous sympathy feeling the success of Satan in this new World, and the sin by Man there committed, resolve to sit no longer confined in Hell, but to follow Satan, their sire, up to the place of Man. To make the way easier from Hell to this World to and fro, they pave a broad highway. . . ."

When the triumphant Satan announces his success to his followers back in Pandemonium, they rise to cheer, but on the instant all, including Satan himself, are turned to hissing, crawling serpents.

In ravaged Eden, the Angel Michael comes and relates to Adam and Eve, for their comfort, all the history that shall be— a summary of the chronicle of the Old Testament up to the New, with Messiah's "Incarnation, Death, Resurrection, and Ascension; the state of the Church till his second coming." But though they are comforted—Eve especially by knowing that from her Seed shall come that Incarnate Messiah at a future time—they must leave the Garden and its ease and beauty and intimate communion with God.

> In either hand the hast'ning Angel caught
> Our lingering parents, and to the eastern gate
> Led them direct, and down the cliff as fast
> To the subjected plain; then disappeared.
> They, looking back, all the eastern side beheld
> Of Paradise, so late their happy seat,
> Waved over by that flaming brand, the gate
> With dreadful faces thronged and fiery arms:
> Some natural tears they dropped, but wiped them soon;
> The world was all before them, where to choose
> Their place of rest, and Providence their guide:
> They, hand in hand, with wandering steps and slow,
> Through Eden took their solitary way.

It is a poignant ending, for they walk from Paradise into the world that man has known in his mortal life ever since, the world we recognize as ours. The Paradise that may be regained awaits in an afterlife. The anticipated tragedies of the world's painful and bloody annals hover over Adam and Eve. It is the birth of history, the dawn of human suffering.

Not interfering with the story, not open enough to draw the wrath of unimaginative censors, the poem nevertheless contains many allusions to the events and disasters that had swirled round Milton. The restored monarchy, corrupt leaders, loose-moraled courtiers all can be seen within the concealment of the poem's story.

The figure of Satan has always fascinated readers of *Paradise Lost* and a good deal of nonsense has been written about him. Some have tried to claim him as the secret hero of the story. But that is to warp Milton's work. An Adversary of God had to be of massive dramatic stature, and it was a triumph that Milton succeeded in drawing him to such a scale. The misinterpretation springs from the tendency in human nature to romanticize the rebel and the fighter against odds. To understand Satan we must not lose sight of the treachery of his rebellion, or against whom it was directed, and how his frustrated rage expresses itself in a cruel effort to destroy creatures who have not harmed him. His speeches are impressively high-sounding but when examined they prove to be boasts and lies. A modern critic, David Daiches, has praised Milton for "exposing . . . all those false romantic notions . . . of heroism as egotistical magnificence . . . the idea that heroic energy in a bad cause is admirable."

The poem is a monumental interpretation, in dramatic metaphors, of the basic Christian teachings about the origins of Man, his nature, his present state, and his future hopes; above all, of the view that he is responsible for his own misfortunes, but that powers beyond his own strength are provided for his salvation if he chooses to avail himself of them.

Chapter 14

"Calm of Mind, All Passion Spent"

QUIET RETIREMENT was the most that John desired. To be once more a celebrity was pleasant but brought its mild annoyances. More people sought him out than he wished to see. Those who came from idle curiosity he would not receive. The same Bishop Burnet who had marveled at his escape from punishment when Charles returned, observed his new fame. He noted that Milton "was much visited by strangers and much admired by all at home for the poems he writ, though he was then blind."

He was in his sixties, now. Blindness and gout made him seem of a greater age than he was. Those who could not presume to call at his house hung about the neighborhood of Artillery Walk. If they were patient they might see the poet led out by his wife for a slow stroll, dressed in a gray cloak and wearing a little silver-hilted sword at his side, an amiable vanity. He seemed frail and walked a little painfully.

His days were busy and regulated with order. Always he rose early. The morning was given over to reading and writing with the aid of his amanuenses. If he visited with those friends whose company he truly liked it was in the afternoon or evening, occasionally at dinner. Music and good conversation delighted him. He was held to be a graceful and interesting talker.

John Dryden called to see him. Milton was pleased. He knew the merits of Dryden's work, even if he scorned him a little as a rhymer. He appreciated the tribute that the other had paid to

Paradise Lost. Praise of one poet for another has sometimes been stifled by rivalry. Dryden had shown himself to be of large spirit.

"Now, Mr. Dryden," John said, entering the room with cautious steps, "it is a surprising pleasure to receive a visit from you."

"I am honored to pay my respects to you, Mr. Milton. I have admired your great poem."

"Your praise of it has been much valued by me, sir."

"It was genuine, Mr. Milton. I can only regret that you did not bring to it, in part at least, the gracefulness of rhyme."

"Sit down, Mr. Dryden," John said. "If we are to talk of rhyme why, then, it might perhaps take us some time. I cannot speak frankly without giving offense to you, I fear, for though I have done poems in rhyme I find it a jingling, surface device not suited to works of length and substance."

"You are a somber man for the literary styles of these days," Dryden said. "You are the last of the Elizabethans, but with the stamp of Oliver and his Puritans upon you which sets you off from them. You do not roister as the Elizabethans did but you share with them the great roll and surge of mighty lines. You are thus a little past your time, sir, if I may be allowed to say so."

"I know that well," John said.

"It is a different England, now," Dryden continued, "and it is not my nature to scorn tastes and fashions, though the court may set them. I have a taste for Shakespeare but my good friends, the people, have not. So, as you would view it, I jingle him for them. It is half my own taste and half a compromise."

"I am not a ready compromiser."

"Clearly not, and I could love you for it. We are opposite creatures, you and I, Mr. Milton. Kings and courts are my natural surroundings. I do not share the harsh distaste you have for them. I do not breathe your moral air. But I like your poem, sir, and have a thing in mind which you will consider a sort of compromise but might yet permit me, in your tolerance."

"What is that, Mr. Dryden?"

"I should like to make a play of your *Paradise Lost,* dividing and altering slightly as the form demands."

"And rhyming?"

"Yes, it would not suit our stage, done otherwise. You might not feel, Mr. Milton, that your poem would benefit by it, but it is of such merit that it cannot be harmed by anything that I might do. So, I am hopeful of your consent."

Milton smiled. "I take it as a compliment, Mr. Dryden, even if one I am unable to appreciate to the full. I confess it seems an idle project to me for a man of your literary powers. But there are many things in the times that I do not understand. So, you may tag my verses, if you like."

They talked long, and Dryden afterward spoke well of him, observing the hardness with which he pronounced his *r's.* "This," he said, "is *litera canina,* the dog letter, and a certain sign of a satirical wit." Out of the conversation came, some time later, a shallow opera called "The State of Innocence and the Fall of Man." In spirit it was like a seventeenth-century musical film version of *Paradise Lost.* John was quite indifferent.

In 1669 one great thorn was removed from his side. He arranged for his daughters to live elsewhere and had them apprenticed "to learn some curious and ingenious sorts of manufacture that are proper for women to learn, particularly embroideries in gold or silver." It was the best he could do for them in this undoubted failure of his personal life. The arrangements cost him a great deal of money and reduced him to the poorest straits that he had ever known. The Restoration and the Fire of London, between them, had hurt his income greatly. His writings brought him little. But he could manage, and the quiet household was a blessing to him.

Since *Paradise Lost,* he had published several scholarly books and been at work upon others; his *History of Britain,* a Latin grammar, a work on logic. In 1671 came two more great poems, published in one volume, *Paradise Regained* and *Samson Agonistes.*

Paradise Regained should not be thought of as a sequel or continuation of *Paradise Lost.* It is a very different sort of poem, though touching the other in certain points. It is a study in self-discipline, a subject of great concern to John. The story is that of Christ's temptation by Satan in the wilderness, when the Devil led Him to the mountaintop and offered the Saviour the cities of the world if He would bow down and worship him.

Here Satan no longer has his wicked glory. The fierce fighter of the other poem has faded down to a somewhat decrepit old man with no real weapon left but his craftiness in the art of false argument. Even though *Paradise Regained* lacks the dramatic story structure of *Paradise Lost* it shows us the final defeat of Satan after the partial victory he had scored in Eden.

Samson Agonistes is a drama in the pure Greek form, with few characters, a chorus, and its chief action off the stage. What more natural for John than to identify himself in some ways with this hero of Israel, betrayed by a woman, blinded and imprisoned, faithful to God, and at last pulling down the hall upon the heads of his enemies, carrying himself and them together to destruction.

Yet it is wrong to make too much of this for the tragedy of Samson results from his own failure, something which Milton would not acknowledge in himself. His first marriage, moreover, may have been a failure but was not a betrayal. The drama strikes closest to John's heart in those speeches where Samson laments his blindness.

Milton had achieved a resignation to his fate. He had been able to say proudly, when his enemies had taunted him with blindness, that "it is not so wretched to be blind as it is not to be capable of enduring blindness." But Samson's voice is the utterance of Milton's bitterness and grief which he had hidden from curious worldly eyes.

> O loss of sight, of thee I most complain!
> Blind among enemies, O worse than chains,
> Dungeon or beggary, or decrepit age!
> Light, the prime work of God, to me is extinct,
> And all her various objects of delight
> Annulled, which might in part my grief have eased;
> Inferior to the vilest now become
> Of man or worm, the vilest here excel me;
> They creep, yet see; I, dark in light, exposed
> To daily fraud, contempt, abuse, and wrong,
> Within doors, or without, still as a fool,
> In power of others, never in my own;
> Scarce half I seem to live, dead more than half.
> Oh, dark, dark, dark, amid the blaze of noon,
> Irrecoverably dark, total eclipse,
> Without all hope of day!

The poet with his gouty joints, his knotted, chalky knuckles, looked back upon the wreck of his political hopes and his narrow escape at the Restoration. How they had failed to appreciate him and rise to the noble challenges he had offered them! He sighs, remembering, of

> . . . the unjust tribunals, under change of times,
> And condemnation of the ungrateful multitude.
> If these they 'scape, perhaps in poverty

With sickness and disease thou bow'st them down,
Painful diseases and deformed,
In crude old age.

It was right that this last poem should close with a line which expressed the fulfillment of his work. He knew he had accomplished his high ministry. What else would follow he could now await,

. . . calm of mind, all passion spent.

There were still disturbances. Some Royalists had not forgotten their hatred of him, just because he had written a successful poem. It was known that he was far from prosperous. His enemies mocked him for this, as they had mocked him for being blind. Someone wrote a malicious verse in a copy of *Eikonoklastes,* his answer to the King's Book.

That thou escaped'st that vengeance which o'ertook,
Milton, thy regicides and thy own book
Was clemency in Charles beyond compare;
And yet thy doom doth prove more grievous far.
Old, sickly, poor, stark blind, thou writ'st for bread;
So for to live thoud'st call Salmasius from the dead.

To their narrow view, the close of the career of political struggle for Milton seemed no more deep a thing than the loss of bread and butter.

Little flurries of debate still swirled around him; attacks were still heard. And John did not cease his difficult tasks with the completing of his poems. He published another pamphlet on religion, *Of True Religion, Heresy, Schism and Toleration.* In this he denounced corruption as boldly as he ever had, as though, his poems done, it did not matter what might happen to him.

He prepared to publish a volume of his Latin letters of state, written for the Commonwealth. A license was flatly refused. The King would not permit so direct a reminder of the Commonwealth to come before the public. An odd reaction was commencing among the people at large. When the violence of the Restoration had passed, when they had lived for a time under the dissolute Charles, ruled by stern hands that governed with his consent to save him the trouble of being a king, some began to remember the days of Oliver with a kind of wistfulness. Mr. Pepys expressed it nicely, "It is strange how everybody do nowadays reflect upon Oliver and commend him, what brave things he did, and made all the neighbor princes fear him." They were far from fearing the Merry Monarch.

There was another project Milton worked upon, seldom dictating much of it to anyone except his trusted helper, Daniel Skinner. This was a creed, a long thought upon declaration of faith, which he wrote in Latin and called *De Doctrina Christiana, Of Christian Doctrine*. He knew there would be no question of publishing it in his lifetime. Not until 1823 was it finally uncovered and published, during the reign of George IV.

Here John summed up all the secret thoughts, springing from the bitter lessons of his life and his role in the Commonwealth. Here he declared flatly and finally against established state religions, Catholic or Protestant. No men must legislate the faiths of other men. Here he restated and extended his ideas of marriage and the right of divorce. For these secret pages he reserved a doctrine far more startling than that of free divorce. He urged the lawfulness of polygamy, as in the days of the Old Testament patriarchs. Dr. Samuel Johnson, in a famous quip, spoke of the second marriage of a man unhappily wedded before as "the triumph of hope over experience." What, then, should be said of the man who, after the disaster of his first marriage, should in his latter years recommend more than one wife at a time?

John was lacking in humor throughout his life, but here, in this doctrine, we must suspect him of it. When he searches the Old Testament for examples to bear out his argument for polygamy he comes, of course, to Solomon, with his 700 wives and 300 concubines, and *rejects him*. He is a little too much even for this case. "I say nothing of Solomon," observes Milton solemnly, "notwithstanding his wisdom, because he seems to have exceeded due bounds."

Of Christian Doctrine, for all its eccentricities, is his summing up, his pledge of faith in free, searching thought and liberty of worship. There can be no true, inspiring religion without "liberty of thinking and even writing respecting it, according to our individual faith and persuasion. Without this liberty there is neither religion nor gospel—force alone prevails. Without this liberty we are still enslaved. . . ." Remember me, he seems to say, and listen to my words, for they are not easily and lightly set down. "Cultivate truth with brotherly love. Neither adopt my sentiments nor reject them, unless every doubt has been removed from your belief. Farewell." Here he takes leave. Here the road ends. Here the ministry is finished.

Christopher Milton came to see him. John had written, asking him to come. The two had not seen much of one another. Their paths had lain far apart and were daily spreading wider for Christopher, like his grandfather, was now a Roman Catholic. Moreover, he was and always had been, a staunch King's man. In later years he rose to high positions but never held them long. The shadow of his black sheep brother seemed always to haunt him. In 1686, John Evelyn would record in his diary, "New judges also here, among which was Milton, a Papist (brother to that Milton who wrote for the regicides)." He was made a Baron of the Exchequer. Samuel Johnson, who held him in contempt, remarked that "he retired before he had done any disreputable act."

But John had not summoned Christopher from love of his conversation. He was, after all, his brother; and he was a lawyer. John wished him to draw a will.

"Brother," Christopher said reproachfully, "you should have drawn a will before this."

"I had not thought of dying before this," Milton retorted. "Now, I know not what I may do. Anyway, you shall help me. I shall have to speak it to you, as though it were a poem, which," he added grimly, "I fear it is not."

There was a hardness in his tone. "Calm of mind, all passion spent," perhaps, but not all traces of long bitterness purged away.

Christopher had made ready his paper and Milton spoke his wishes. "Brother, the portion due to me from Mr. Powell, my former wife's father, I leave to the unkind children I had by her, but I have received no part of it; and my will and meaning is that they shall have no other benefit of my estate than the said portion and what I have besides done for them, they having been very undutiful to me. And all the residue of my estate I leave to the disposal of Elizabeth, my loving wife."

His brother was shocked. "John," he said, "this will look badly and reflect ill upon you."

John was firm. "Leave it as I say," he said irritably. "Before God I feel I am doing no injustice. If I have erred in anything it was not through malice but through confusion and torment. They are well placed now, and at much cost to me, in more than money. Let it be."

He had closed accounts with these three women he could not understand, borne him by the woman he had not understood.

"Now then," he added, to Christopher, "there is little more that I shall wish to do. The treasures of my books are now well stored within me or are lost to me. My work is done. I cannot maintain these idle shelves and employ more persons to read

to me the things I will not need again. If you will help me I
shall sell them, at least the greater part of them, such as I will
not take comfort from merely holding in my hands again. It is
better that I should do this now. Elizabeth will not know how
to get for them what they are worth."

The gout was striking in, afflicting him with pain and fever.
He was sixty-five years old. He stayed much in his bed, now,
and felt weakness creeping over him. On the eighth of November, 1674, he seemed much worse. His fever was high. Nathan
Paget came twice to see him in the forenoon. When he had left
the first time, Cyriack and Edward Phillips came to the house.
John talked weakly with them, and cheerfully. They brought
him word that Andrew Marvell would be there in the evening.
In the afternoon he slept, more restfully than he had done for
days. When Elizabeth came to rouse him, he was dead. On the
twelfth, he was buried beside his father, in the chancel of St.
Giles, Cripplegate.

In long after years, admiring Wordsworth wrote

> Milton! thou shouldst be living at this hour:
> England hath need of thee: she is a fen
> Of stagnant waters: altar, sword, and pen,
> Fireside, the heroic wealth of hall and bower,
> Have forfeited their ancient English dower
> Of inward happiness. We are selfish men;
> Oh! raise us up, return to us again;
> And give us manners, virtue, freedom, power.
> Thy soul was like a Star, and dwelt apart:
> Thou hadst a voice whose sound was like the sea:
> Pure as the naked heavens, majestic, free
> So didst thou travel on life's common way,
> In cheerful godliness; and yet thy heart
> The lowliest duties on herself did lay.

If not a wholly accurate description, still the tribute is his due, however much, like other men, he fought one kind of oppression only to find himself allied with another; however much, like other men, he stooped in personal relations to bitternesses below the level of his lofty visions. Still, his fidelity to the concept of freedom, religious and political, his memorable words about it in poetry and prose, endure as the inspiration that prompted Wordsworth's homage.

Yet it is not the Milton of public affairs, Oliver's secretary, controversialist and pamphleteer, who is immortal. That man might be a mere footnote to history. He who lives is the poet, the master of word and image, of majestic song. It is he who ventured and achieved "Things unattempted yet in prose or rhyme." It is he whose voice is heard, living, in this hour, and will be heard as long as the English tongue shall last.

Index